ArtScroll Youth Series®

TALES OF

by G. MaTov

translated by
Shaindel Weinbach

illustrated by
Miriam Bardugo

TZADDIKIM

A wonderful collection of stories from our Sages
and the great Torah and Chassidic leaders,
arranged according to the Sidra of the week.

Published by

Mesorah Publications, ltd

in conjunction with

HAMESORAH /
Jerusalem

FIRST EDITION
First Impression . . . March 1988
SECOND EDITION
First Impression . . . January 1999

Published and Distributed by
MESORAH PUBLICATIONS, Ltd.
Brooklyn, New York 11223
in conjunction with
HAMESORAH / Jerusalem

Distributed in Israel by
MESORAH MAFITZIM / J. GROSSMAN
Rechov Harav Uziel 117
Jerusalem, Israel

Distributed in Europe by
J. LEHMANN HEBREW BOOKSELLERS
20 Cambridge Terrace
Gateshead, Tyne and Wear
England NE8 1RP

THE ARTSCROLL YOUTH SERIES ·
TALES OF TZADDIKIM / VOL. III — VAYIKRA
© *Copyright 1988 by* MESORAH PUBLICATIONS, Ltd.
1969 Coney Island Avenue / Brooklyn, N.Y. 11223 / (718) 339-1700

ISBN:
0-89906-829-4 (hard cover)

Printed in the United States of America by Noble Book Press Corp.
Bound by Sefercraft Quality Bookbinders, Ltd., Brooklyn, N.Y.

Table of Contents

◆§ Parashas Shemini

◆§ Parashas Tazriya

◆§ Parashas Metzora

◁§ Parashas Behukosay

◁§ Special Haftaros

TALES OF
TZADDIKIM

פָּרָשַׁת וַיִּקְרָא

Parashas Vayikra

The Leper at the Palace

"וַיִּקְרָא אֶל מֹשֶׁה"

And He called to Moshe (1:1)

A gentile once said to R' Elazar with a sneer, "More than *Hashem* loved Moshe your teacher, He loved Bilam."

"What do you mean?! Do you really think that *Hashem* favored the wicked Bilam over our saintly Moshe?!" said R' Elazar in astonishment. "Tell me, on what do you base such a statement?"

The gentile had a ready answer, "Why it says so clearly in your own Torah. When *Hashem* wished to speak to Moshe He summoned him to the *Mishkan*. But, when He wished to speak to Bilam — it says: 'And *Hashem* appeared to Bilam.' He did not summon him, not wishing to bother him, but came to him. This shows that *Hashem* respected and loved Bilam more than Moshe! There you have it," he said with a note of victory in his voice.

"You misunderstand it," R' Elazar said. "Listen to the following parable and I am sure that you will change your mind."

He began: "A leper once reached the king's palace and

wished to enter. He began pounding on the gates, making a commotion, shouting, 'Let me in! Let me in!' The noise and shouting reached the king's ears. 'Who is making such a disturbance?' he demanded angrily. 'Oh it is some leper who wishes to enter the palace,' the king was told.

"'A leper wishes to enter the royal palace?!' the king said in amazement. 'That is unheard of! He must be disposed of. But, if I send a servant out to chase him away, he will seize the opportunity and force his way into the palace. He is liable to endanger us all. What can we do?' he asked.

"The king himself found the solution. 'I will go to the gate in person and tell the leper to go away; he will surely obey me out of respect and fear.'

"The king rose from his throne and went to the palace gates. He could hear the madman raving and ranting, demanding to be admitted into the palace. The king drew near and said: 'Be gone. Do not dare show your face here again. Don't you dare contaminate any of us. If you do not leave at once, you will regret your rashness!'

"At these words the leper turned pale. He did not wait for the king to carry out his threats, but picked up his heels and ran."

"But," continued R' Elazar, "when the king's good friend comes to the palace and knocks upon the gate, the king then, too, wishes to know who has arrived. When the gatekeeper announces that his friend is there, the king wants to let him know that he is welcome. He calls out to him and says, 'Come in, dear friend. Please, won't you come in.' You can hear the friendliness and warmth in his voice. Since this visitor is very close to him, the king is not satisfied that a mere gatekeeper should admit him but he calls out and invites him in personally.

"The parallel should be clear," he said to the gentile. "Bilam is like that leper who pounded angrily upon the palace gates, demanding to be admitted. What does *Hashem* reply to this? 'I will go myself to the palace gates and deal with him, lest he strike someone down and force his way into the palace. He must not be allowed to contaminate anyone.' And so He goes, personally, to speak to Bilam.

"But Moshe Rabbenu is the welcome friend who comes to the palace. When the Master of the Universe hears his voice, He calls out to him to come inside, to enter the Tent of Meeting, the *Ohel Moed*, which is like the royal palace. Only a very dear friend receives such an invitation.

"And now," R' Elazar concluded, "do you still insist that *Hashem* loves Bilam more than Moshe Rabbenu?"

(*Zohar* to *Parashas Balak*)

Unable or Unwilling?

"יַקְרִיב אֹתוֹ לִרְצֹנוֹ"

He shall sacrifice him willingly (1:3)

...He is coerced until he says that he is willing.

(*Tractate Rosh Hashanah 6a*)

The *Yehudi Hakadosh* and his disciple, R' Simcha Bunim of Pshischa, were once walking together along a country road. Suddenly a farmer came rushing up to them, begging them to help him.

He pointed to a large wagon in the distance and said urgently, "My wagon of hay has overturned and the hay has scattered. Can you lend me a hand?"

They looked at the scattered bundles of hay, shook their heads and said, "We cannot help you. It is a hopeless task."

"Oh yes, you could," said the farmer, "if you would only want to, you certainly could! You just don't want to!"

He turned around and went back to the wagon where he began loading the hay on himself.

The *Yehudi Hakadosh* turned to his disciple and said, "Did you hear that farmer? He said that if we really wanted to, we could do the job. If we really were sincere about serving *Hashem*, then nothing would stand in our way, nothing would seem impossible. Nothing would seem too difficult. But," he sighed, "we don't want to. That is why we make excuses and say that we cannot."

Tefillin for Charity

"כָּל־חֵלֶב לַה'"

All the fat is Hashem's (3:16)

R' Avraham Mordechai, the Gerrer Rebbe, was sitting at his table, engrossed in study, when there was a knock at the door.

"Come in!" he called.

A poor man came in, dressed in rags. He wanted

tzedakah. The Rebbe was about to give him some money when, suddenly, he changed his mind.

"Wait a moment," he said.

He went into an adjoining room and came back with a small package — the *tefillin* which the saintly R' Moshe of Pshersk had written. Many people had offered the Rebbe huge sums for this special pair of *tefillin*, but the Rebbe had refused them all. Now, the Rebbe placed the precious pair of *tefillin* in the hands of the poor man, saying, "Here. Take these. They are yours. I advise you to bring them to my brother, the saintly R' Moshe Bezalel, who will surely pay you a fortune for them. He has had his eye on them for a long time. The money which he gives you for them will be enough for you to support yourself and your family for a long time. Buy yourself some merchandise and set up a business. Then you will never have to go begging again."

The poor man thanked the Rebbe heartily and rushed off to the home of R' Moshe Bezalel where a fortune awaited him.

Some time later the two brothers met. R' Moshe Bezalel asked his brother, "Tell me, why did you give that poor man your most precious possession, the sacred pair of *tefillin*? Could you not have given him money instead?"

R' Avraham Mordechai replied, "The Torah teaches us that we must give to *Hashem* the fat of every sacrifice, the *chelev*. Our Sages apply this to everything which a person owns. One must give the fat, the best, of what he possesses to *Hashem*, that is, to dedicate it for a *mitzvah*. The most precious possession I had at the time that this unfortunate Jew came to me was that pair of *tefillin*. This, then, is what I gave him, thus sanctifying my possession by dedicating it to *Hashem*, for the *mitzvah* of charity!"

The Egg Goes to Court

"וְכָל־דָּם לֹא תֹאכֵלוּ"

You shall not eat any blood (3:17)

Some gentiles once accused the Jews of a town in Eastern Europe of having murdered a Christian child in order to use his blood for baking *matzos*.

The matter was brought to court. The rabbi of the community defended the Jews who had been so falsely accused. While the case was in progress, he turned to the judge and made a request, "May I be allowed to bring someone to court?" The judge nodded. The rabbi then said, "Tell one of the guards to bring in a Jewish woman off the street. Any woman will do." Before long the guard had returned with a simple Jewish housewife, shopping basket in hand. She looked startled.

The rabbi handed her an egg and said, "Will you be so good as to fry me an egg?"

The woman cracked the egg open and, before pouring its contents into a frying pan, examined it carefully for bloodspots.

"Will you tell the court why you were examining the egg," said the rabbi.

"That is how I always open an egg. I first look to see if it has any blood spots before using it," answered the woman.

The rabbi smiled in satisfaction, then turned back to the judge. "Do you see, Your Honor? Even a simple Jewish woman will not use an egg if it contains blood. Do you really believe, then, that we Jews are capable of baking *matzos* with blood?"

The Lesson of the Snuffbox

"אֲשֶׁר נָשִׂיא יֶחֱטָא"

If a prince shall sin (4:22)

R' Chaim Yosef David Azulai, better known as the Chida, enjoyed taking snuff.

Once he traveled to France to raise money for the Jewish community in *Eretz Yisrael*. Wherever he went, people vied over the privilege of playing host to this distinguished, prominent personality from the Holy Land. Two of the community's wealthy and respected citizens were granted the honor. The Chida was to sleep in the home of one and eat in the home of the other. For this privilege, they each agreed to contribute handsomely for the Jews of *Eretz Yisrael*.

Friday night came and with it the *Shabbos* meal. The atmosphere at the table was one of such warmth that no one realized how wet and stormy it was outside.

When it came time for the Chida to go to his night lodgings, the host and his guest had to brave fierce winds and rains as they wound through the city streets before reaching their destination. The Chida thanked his dinner host who turned around and went home. The Chida went inside. Here his second host showed him to a comfortable room. The Chida sank gratefully into the soft bed and was soon fast asleep.

He awoke in the middle of the night and fumbled for his snuffbox. It was not on the table by his bedside. He got up and rummaged around among his things. Then he remembered; he had forgotten it on the table in the home of his first host. He could not do without his snuff!

He felt that he could not wait until morning. He must have a pinch of snuff right away.

The Chida dressed quickly and left the house. The rain had turned to snow. He shivered as he made his way through the streets until he came to the first host's home. He knocked on the door, softly at first. But when no one came, he began knocking louder and louder until he was almost pounding. Rubbing sleepy eyes, the host came to the door. Opening it, he was surprised to see his guest.

"What is the matter?" he asked in concern. "Why have you come so urgently in the middle of the night?"

The Chida stepped inside, reassuring the man, "Oh it is nothing important. It is just that I forgot my snuffbox here last night and I longed for a pinch."

The host sighed in relief. Then he turned to look for the snuffbox. It was not on the table. He went to his bedroom to ask his wife if she had seen it. She said that she had put it away in the closet with the silver and locked it. The servant had the key.

The master now went to wake up the servant. Finally, he returned to the shivering guest with the trophy.

The Chida thanked him profusely and left. He hurried back to the bed which he had lately left and placed the snuffbox safely on the table by his side.

He should have fallen asleep right away. But he tossed and turned. Something was bothering him. He reviewed the events of the past hour and was very dissatisfied with his behavior. "Look at what I did," he thought. "Look at all the people whom I disturbed, just to satisfy my craving for some snuff! I woke up my kind host, alarming him, then causing him and his wife and servant discomfort, as he searched for my snuffbox. People who had worked hard on Friday, had to lose sleep over my petty habit. How could I have done such a thing? I am ashamed of myself!"

The Chida could not bring himself to touch his snuffbox. Sleep evaded him as waves of remorse washed over him. He eagerly awaited the morrow when he might make amends for his disgraceful behavior.

As soon as he felt that the townspeople were up, he asked the *shammash* of the synagogue to go through the city announcing that the visitor from *Eretz Yisrael* would give a speech in the central synagogue right after prayers. He requested that everyone attend.

Everyone flocked to the main *beis haknesses*, eager and curious to hear what the learned visitor had to say.

To everyone's surprise, the Chida stood before them on the *bimah* weeping.

With tears streaming down his cheeks, the Chida related the events of the previous night, then said: "My dear friends, I have always realized my lowliness and baseness, my lack of worth. But now, when I think of my actions of last night, I am convinced that I am lower than the dust upon which you tread. I was not able to control my desire for even a little while, but had to give in to my whim. Even though it was the middle of the night, I disturbed the sleep of good, kind people just to satisfy my ridiculous craving. How am I any better than an animal which also pursues its desires without letting anything stand in its way?" His words echoed through the large hall.

He was overcome and had to stop to compose himself. He was soon able to continue. "I feel obliged to publicly announce, therefore, that if you wish to show your love for *Eretz Yisrael*, by all means do so, by giving generously to help support its community of Torah scholars. But, by no means must you show me any honor or deference or give for my sake! I am totally unworthy of your respect!"

He now turned towards the eastern wall, where his hosts occupied a prominent place. "I must now beg forgiveness, from you and from your families and all your servants whose sleep I foolishly disturbed. And to show you how truly repentant I am, I hereby announce, before all the people present here, that from today on, I promise never to take any snuff again!"

The people gathered in the synagogue listened openmouthed. A rabbi and *tzaddik* was actually asking forgiveness. Everyone was deeply moved. His sincerity touched their hearts and they, too, burst into tears, each one feeling ashamed of his personal shortcomings. Soon the entire congregation was weeping.

For years to come, the townspeople were to recall that memorable sermon, their private *Shabbos* of Repentance — in the middle of winter!

The Rebbe Must Also Repent!

"אֲשֶׁר נָשִׂיא יֶחֱטָא"

If a prince shall sin (4:22)

Asher is related to the word ashrei, fortunate. Fortunate is
the generation whose prince or leader takes care to bring
an atonement, (even) for an unintentional sin.

(Rashi)

The saintly Rebbe, the Shpole Zeide, looked very
disturbed.

He heaved a heavy sigh and said, "I am afraid that I lit
candles too late today. I may have desecrated the *Shabbos*!
That is why you see me so troubled."

The chasidim tried to comfort him, one by one.

"Surely no evil can befall a *tzaddik*."

"Maybe there was some mistake about the time."

"*Hashem* protects His loved ones and does not let them
stumble."

Each chasid had his own words of consolation. Each,
except for Reb Refael, a man known for his
uncompromising honesty. Reb Refael did not say
anything, if he did not mean it sincerely. He did not say
anything, unless he was certain that what he said was
absolutely true. Now that his turn had come, all eyes
were fixed upon him. How would he comfort the
anguished Rebbe?

Reb Refael of Barashid stood up. He looked directly at
the Rebbe and said, "There is no doubt that the Rebbe
must repent. Is the possibility of *chillul Shabbos* a thing to
be taken lightly, even if it is questionable and not
certain?!"

He had spoken his mind and sat down again.

The Rebbe had heard. His eyes lit up with their usual sparkle; he turned to all the chasidim and rebuked them, "And to think that because of your reassurances I might have died without repenting!"

The Fruits that Brought Pain

"אֲשֶׁר נָשִׂיא יֶחֱטָא"

If a prince shall sin (4:22)

Asher *is related to the word* ashrei, *fortunate. Fortunate is the generation whose prince or leader takes care to bring an atonement, (even) for an unintentional sin.*

(Rashi)

R' Zalman, like his brother, the famous R' Chaim of Volozhin, was also a disciple of the Gaon of Vilna. One time, as he was sitting in the *beis medrash* deeply engrossed, a man came up to him with a copy of Tractate *Demai* in his hand and a broad smile upon his face. "I have hit upon an excellent explanation here." He was a Lithuanian Jew who pronounced the letter *shin* like a *sin* and when he said '*peirush*', explanation, it sounded like '*peirus*' or '*fruit*'. He enthusiastically explained what he considered a brilliant insight.

R' Zalman saw that the man had not understood the *mishnah* at all and was just babbling. R' Zalman was annoyed and said pointedly, "Excuse me sir, but your *peirus* are *peirus demai*," (fruits of *demai* are the fruits of an unlearned person). The man was not too stupid to understand that his explanation had been termed meaningless. He shut the *mishnah* and turned away, deeply insulted.

R' Zalman had not realized that he had spoken so sharply. He surely had not intended to hurt the well-meaning man, but had spoken impulsively. And, if the man had misunderstood the *mishnah*, who was he, R' Zalman, to embarrass him so callously? He should have, rather, corrected his mistake and shown him how the *mishnah* was to be understood, instead of making a clever but caustic remark. He jumped up to seek out the man and ask forgiveness, but he was no longer there. R' Zalman felt terrible. He must apologize.

He questioned all the people in the *beis medrash*, but no one remembered any such person.

From that day on, R' Zalman knew no peace. Each day he would go to the marketplace, or wander the streets of Vilna, in search of the man whom he had embarrassed. He looked high and low, but could find no clue as to his identity or whereabouts. It seemed that he must have been a one-time visitor to Vilna who had left the city right after the incident.

Still, R' Zalman would not be comforted. He was so disturbed by his shameful behavior that he took to his bed. His family saw how troubled R' Zalman was. Finally, his father-in-law, R' Michel Peslis, decided that some way must be found to get R' Zalman's mind off the incident.

He finally thought of a plan. R' Michel had a friend, a man who was clever and alert. R' Michel begged this friend to go to R' Zalman, pretending that he was the Lithuanian *am ha'aretz*. He was to say that he had heard that R' Zalman was looking for him. So much time had passed since the incident that R' Zalman surely must have forgotten the man's face.

The friend came to R' Zalman and stretched out his hand in welcome. "Don't you remember me? I once told you an explanation of a *mishnah* in *Demai* and you, jokingly, said that my *peirus* were fruits of *demai*."

R' Zalman was not one to be taken in so easily. He sensed that this scene was being staged for his benefit. Turning to the fellow, he said, "Tell me, are you really that man whom I embarrassed or do you just want to make me feel good? If you are fooling me, you are heaping insult on injury and only making me feel worse!" The man realized that there was no longer any point in continuing with the game and admitted that he had been sent by R' Zalman's father-in-law.

R' Zalman felt all the worse. He grieved and his health continued to suffer. Finally even his master, the Gaon of Vilna, learned of the matter. R' Eliyahu summoned his pupil and attempted to comfort him. "You have already done all in your power to find the man whom you wronged," he said. "What more can you do? After a man sincerely regrets an evil deed and reaches the limit of his own powers in trying to right the wrong *Hashem* helps him and gives him heavenly assistance in overcoming his *yetzer hara*. But if he leaves ground uncovered, if he does not explore every single avenue, then *Hashem* does not intervene and help him.

"My son, *Hashem* surely sees how determined you were to find this man, in order to beg his forgiveness and repair the wrong you did to him. There is nothing more that you can do; you have done everything in your power. I am certain that *Hashem* will instill in that man's heart the desire to forgive you."

R' Zalman heard the words of assurance which his teacher had said and finally felt at peace with himself.

Forgiveness at the Bar Mitzvah

"אֲשֶׁר נָשִׂיא יֶחֱטָא"

If a prince shall sin (4:22)

Asher *is related to the word* ashrei, *fortunate. Fortunate is the generation whose prince or leader takes care to bring an atonement, (even) for an unintentional sin.*

(Rashi)

It was a happy occasion for all the participants — the guests, family and the *bar mitzvah* boy himself. The hall in Bnei Brak buzzed with congratulations and greetings when, suddenly, everything was silent. A small figure stood in the doorway, an old man, familiar to all Bnei Brak residents even though he hardly went out any more.

Everyone rose to show their respect to the great man. It was the Steipler Rav, R' Yaakov Yisrael Kanievsky. Already in his eighties, he no longer attended *simchah*s in his own family! What, then, was he doing here?

The riddle was soon solved. The Steipler asked if he could have a few words alone with the *bar mitzvah* boy.

The two went to a small room where they could speak in private. A few minutes later, they emerged and the Steipler left the hall.

The *bar mitzvah* boy was, immediately, besieged by a bombardment of questions. What had the Steipler wanted of him? What had he said?

Overcome with excitement, the *bar mitzvah* boy barely managed to emit, "He asked me for *mechilah*, forgiveness."

The boy's father, it turned out, *davened* in the same *beis medrash* as the Steipler, the Lederman Shul. Six years earlier, when the lad was a mere seven-year-old, the Steipler had seen him holding a large *sefer* during prayers and had mistaken it for a *chumash*. He had thought the boy was learning when he should have been praying and had rebuked him for doing so. The child was taken aback. Too confused to reply, he had held up the large book. The Steipler could see that it was, in fact, a *siddur*! He wished to apologize immediately, but knew that according to *halachah*, a young child's forgiveness has no real meaning.

And so, the Steipler had asked for the name of the child and his age — and waited. Seven years later, he had made inquiries as to when and where the boy would be celebrating his *bar mitzvah*. When that day arrived, he had waited until after nightfall; the boy was now thirteen and at last, could legally accept an apology.

That is when the saintly Steipler Rav hurried to the hall and formally asked to be forgiven.

Self Erasing Notebook

"וְהִתְוַדָּה אֲשֶׁר חָטָא"

And he shall confess what he sinned (5:5)

The two holy brothers, R' Elimelech of Lizensk and R' Zusha of Anipoli had a third brother who ran a tavern.

R' Zusha and R' Elimelech knew that, outwardly, their brother was a man who worked hard for his living and did not devote much time to the study of Torah and the worship of G-d. But, they felt that he was special and wished to see how his unusual qualities expressed themselves in his daily life. And so, they came to pay him a visit.

They found him busy behind his bar, serving his many gentile customers. This one wanted whiskey, that one beer. He had to pour, wash the drinking glasses, take money and give change. But what was special about him? What could they learn from him? They kept watch for the rest of the day. He seemed to be just like any other tavern keeper. But they did notice one unusual thing. From time to time, they saw him jotting something down in a notebook. Nightfall came and the tavern was closed. R' Elimelech and R' Zusha went to bed disappointed. They had, as yet, learned nothing. And, then, they heard strange sounds; someone was weeping. A moment later, they heard the sound of blows. Someone was being beaten!

They jumped out of bed and ran to the next room.

There they found their brother in tears. And he was striking himself!

"What are you doing?" they asked.

Tears still coursing down his cheeks, the brother replied. "Do you see this notebook?" he asked them. "During the day, whenever I have an impure thought or do not behave in the best possible way, I jot down my sins here. Then, at night, when I have time to think, I review all of my shortcomings and do *teshuvah*. I weep bitterly and beat myself, until I see that my repentance has been accepted. Only then do I allow myself to lie down for the night."

"But how do you know when your repentance is complete?" they asked.

"That is simple enough," he replied, pointing to his notebook. "When I see that the writing on the page has disappeared, I know that my sins have been forgiven and my *teshuvah* has been accepted in heaven."

A Different Reason

"אוֹ מָצָא אֲבֵדָה... וְהֵשִׁיב"

Or if he found a lost thing... he shall return it ((5:22,23)

One day when the Empress of Rome returned from her daily walk, she suddenly realized that she had lost her expensive jewels on the way. She sent her maids to search for them, but they returned emptyhanded. The empress was distraught.

She ordered the town crier to proclaim that whoever found the jewels within thirty days would be handsomely rewarded. However, if someone were to find them and hand them over after the thirty days, he would be put to death!

The town crier walked through the streets of Rome, blowing his trumpet and making his proclamation.

Thirty days went by, but no one came forward with the lost jewels. The empress was beside herself with sorrow. These had been her favorite gems. Had someone found them and kept them?

On the thirty-first day a page came to the empress announcing that a rabbi wished to see the empress. He claimed to have found her jewels. The empress was beside herself with joy and had him brought before her at once.

The sage, R' Shmuel ben Sosarti, had, indeed, found the missing jewels and now gave them to the empress.

"When did you find these?" she asked him.

"Thirty-one days ago, on the very day when the empress lost them." he replied.

"Did you not hear the proclamation made throughout the city streets?"

"Yes, I heard it."

"I see you are a stranger to Rome. Perhaps you did not understand the proclamation. Please repeat it to me."

R' Shmuel repeated it word for word. The empress was confused. He had found it on the day that she had lost it and held on to it for thirty-one days.

"Tell me," she asked, "why did you not return them right away? You knew, that by coming after the deadline, you were risking your life. If you had brought them yesterday you would have received a reward!"

R' Shmuel explained. "Your Majesty, I did not want you to think that I was returning your lost jewelry because of the reward offered, or because I feared you. There is one reason and one reason only. In our Torah we are commanded to return lost objects to their proper owner. *That* is why I brought back the empress's jewels!"

The empress was deeply impressed. She exclaimed: "Blessed be the G-d of your people!" And R' Shmuel, to be sure, was not taken away to be executed!

(According to *Yerushalmi Bava Metzia* 2:5)

"I Didn't Buy a Precious Stone"

"אוֹ מָצָא אֲבֵדָה... וְהֵשִׁיב"

Or if he found a lost thing... he shall return it (5:22,23)

The *tana* R' Shimon Ben Shetach was one of our people's great leaders. He had many disciples who eagerly drank in every word of his Torah. And yet, this same R' Shimon insisted that he support himself by the work of his own hands.

His *talmidim* saw how hard he labored and begged him to accept money from them, but he always refused. Once, they said to him, "Rebbe, allow us to put together enough money to buy you a good, strong donkey. The beast will help you earn your livelihood."

R' Shimon agreed. Overjoyed, the students did not wait for him to change his mind, but rushed right out to the marketplace to buy a good donkey. They met an Arab leading a sturdy animal. Learning that it was for sale, they examined the beast carefully and paid the Arab.

They were leading the animal back to R' Shimon when one of them saw a precious stone on the donkey's lead rope. They rushed back to their master to tell him the good news.

"Rebbe! Now you will never have to work again!" they shouted.

"Why?" asked R' Shimon.

"We bought a donkey from an Arab and found a precious stone tied around its neck. If you sell it, you will have enough to support you till the end of your days!"

R' Shimon smiled at their enthusiasm, but shook his head. "No, my dear *talmidim*. You mean well. But I bought a donkey. Not a precious gem. Go and return it to the seller."

Crestfallen, they went back to find the seller. When they gave the gem to the Arab and told him that they had found it tied to his donkey's neck, he exclaimed in surprise, "Blessed be the G-d of R' Shimon ben Shetach!"

The students returned to R' Shimon and repeated the Arab's words. He smiled broadly and said, "It is better," he said, "to hear an Arab praising the G-d of our people than to find all the precious gems in the world!"

(According to *Yerushalmi, Bava Metzia Perek* 2:5)

Chickens that Became Goats

"אוֹ מָצָא אֲבֵדָה... וְהֵשִׁיב"

Or if he found a lost thing... he shall return it (5:22,23)

Aman was once walking through the streets of a strange city carrying a basket of live chickens on his back, when he decided to stop for a rest. He put his burden down for a while, ate something and then, started on his way, forgetting all about his basket of chickens.

The birds began crowing and cackling. R' Chanina ben Dosa's wife looked out of her nearby doorway to see what was happening. She picked up the basket of chickens and brought them to her husband.

R' Chanina said, "Someone must have left them here by mistake and forgotten them. Take them into the yard and we will care for them. We will just have to wait until that person comes back for them. If he gives the proper signs of identification, we will give him his chickens. But we must not have any benefit from these chickens. We must not use any of their eggs!"

From that day on, R' Chanina and his wife cared for the chickens. They fed them and watered them, cleaned the chicken coop and protected them from cats and weasels. In time, they laid eggs. The chickens sat on the eggs and in time they hatched into small, puff-ball chicks. The air was full of their piping squeaks and the accompanying squawks of the mother hens, herding them together. It was lively! The chickens would at times make their way into the house and dirty it.

"We have no choice," decided R' Chanina. "We must sell these chickens. With the money we can buy goats instead. Goats will be much easier to care for. We can send them into the nearby woods to graze by themselves. Then at night they will return to their pen. We will have to milk them, of course, but we can sell the milk and buy more goats. Goats are not as difficult to care for."

But their wicked neighbors accused the goats of eating from their fields.

"If what you say is true," said R' Chanina, "let bears come out of the woods and eat the goats. But if they are innocent, then let each goat return home from grazing with a bear impaled upon its horns!"

The next morning the goats went out to graze, as usual. That evening, the goats returned, each goat carrying a heavy bear upon its horns!!!

Time passed and the man who had misplaced his chickens happened to be walking with a friend past R' Chanina's house. The place looked familiar to him. He stopped at the doorway and suddenly remembered! "This is the spot where I put down my basket of chickens," he said to his friend. R' Chanina heard him and rushed out.

"Are you really the man who left a basket of chickens here a few years ago?" he asked excitedly.

"Yes, I am," said the man. "The basket had a small hole on one side and the chickens were tied with a red string."

R' Chanina was satisfied that this was the orginal owner. He said, "Come inside. I have something for you. I think that you will be very satisfied."

R' Chanina opened the gate and led him in; the man followed. However, to his surprise, R' Chanina led him not to a chicken coop, but to a goat pen. The small pen teemed with goats of all sizes and colors!

The man could not understand. "What does this have to do with me and my chickens?" he asked.

R' Chanina smiled. "Do you see these goats? They are all yours! I bought them from the money I got by selling your chickens and their chicks — a few generations of chickens, in fact!"

(According to *Taanis 25a*)

R' Binyamin Beinish's Tehillim

"עַם־זוּ יָצַרְתִּי... תְּהִלָּתִי יְסַפֵּרוּ"

'This nation which I created... they tell My praises'
(Haftorah Parashas Vayikra, Yeshaya 43:21)

The Rebbe of Lubavitch, the *Tzemach Tzedek*, stayed awake all night, studying Torah. When day dawned, he prayed for several hours. Then, still wrapped in his *tallis* and wearing his *tefillin*, he would sit down to resume his study.

The *beis haknesses* was empty except for the rebbe. For many hours he was alone, until another man entered.

It was Reb Binyamin Beinish, a man who lived in a village not far from Lubavitch. He had been traveling with a friend, Reb Yitzchak Shaul, to sell their produce together today, market day, in the city of Lubavitch. He had been lucky; he had sold all of his farm produce by an early hour. After completing his work, he went to the local *beis medrash* to recite some *Tehillim*. His friend would know where to find him.

He began pouring his heart into the moving words of the *Tehillim*. He said each word as if it were a precious pearl which he was giving to his Maker, in thanks for all the kindness He had shown to him. His sweet voice sang with fervor, the notes pouring forth like honey.

The Lubavitcher Rebbe heard these lovely notes. He looked around him, wondering, "Who can be singing so beautifully? Who is putting such deep feelings into the words of King David?" He got up to look around for the source of the heavenly melody.

He spied the simple villager, hunched over the worn volume of *Tehillim*, and was overcome with emotion. The Rebbe burst into tears!

"What innocence! What perfect prayer! What wholesome feeling!"

Just at this moment another Jew happened to enter the *beis medrash*, the famous Reb Efraim Yaffe of Kopost. The Rebbe turned to this chasid, the tears still wet upon his cheeks, and declared: "If only I could say even *one* verse of *Tehillim* with the same simple freshness as that villager!"

The Villager's Tehillim

"עַם־זוּ יָצַרְתִּי... תְּהִלָּתִי יְסַפֵּרוּ"

I have created this nation... they shall recite My praises
(Haftorah Parashas Vayikra, Yeshaya 43:21)

In the times of the saintly Baal Shem Tov a heavenly decree was passed against the Jews. One Jewish community was to be totally destroyed!

The leader of his generation, the Baal Shem Tov, felt personally responsible. Who would save this city if not he? Who knew about this terrible decree? The Baal Shem Tov had his soul soar up to heaven, so that he could learn more about the grave danger threatening his brethren. To his dismay, he learned that there was nothing that he could do to save them. The decree had been sealed. It was final!

On its way back down to earth, the Baal Shem Tov's soul passed through the various palaces in heaven. Among them was one that shone with a brilliant light, far brighter than all the palaces surrounding it. Each palace belonged to a certain *tzaddik*, he knew. Who, he wondered, had built such a magnificent palace here in heaven?!

He asked and was told that it belonged to a villager who was still alive. This Jew recited the entire Book of *Tehillim* five times daily! It was the letters of his prayers that sparkled and glowed, illuminating that palace so brightly.

The Baal Shem Tov's soul returned to earth. He went at once to the village where this simple, but great man, lived and spoke to him, "If you only knew how great was your merit, if you only realized that the merit of your *Tehillim* was great enough to save an entire community, wouldn't you do your utmost to save all of those people?"

Without hesitation, the villager replied, "I am surprised to learn that I have a place at all in the World to Come. But since you say that I do, I will certainly be glad to give it away to save my people!"

These words were no sooner uttered, then the sealed decree was annulled and the people saved.

The Din Torah

"הַזְכִּירֵנִי נִשָּׁפְטָה יָחַד סַפֵּר אַתָּה לְמַעַן תִּצְדָּק"

Put Me in remembrance, let us be judged together, declare, that
you may be justified
(Haftorah Parashas Vayikra, Yeshaya 43:26)

They were both great men, leaders of communities, R' David of Mir and R' David of Novardok. But as sometimes happens, they had a difference of opinion. The only way to solve their differences was to go to court, to a *beis din*, for a *din Torah*. Together, they decided to take their case to the famous R' Chaim of Volozhin.

R' Chaim listened to both sides very carefully and decided in favor of R' David of Mir. R' David of Novardok tried again to convince R' Chaim that he was really right, but the decision stood.

R' David accepted the ruling, but, deep in his heart, could not help bearing a grudge against R' Chaim. R' Chaim sensed this and decided to do something about it.

In those days, it was customary for Torah leaders to gather together to discuss important communal matters that concerned all of Jewry. They used to convene these meetings whenever there was a seasonal trade fair in the large city of Zalva. Since everyone considered R' Chaim of Volozhin the leader of his generation, all the other rabbis would go forth together to greet him when he came and would then go to him, one by one, to offer their personal good wishes.

At the gathering which took place after the *din Torah*, R' David of Novardok was among those who received R' Chaim. He did not want anyone to know that he bore R' Chaim a grudge, least of all, R' Chaim himself. Later, as they were sitting together, chatting about mutual interests, R' Chaim asked R' David, "I have just been asked to settle a difficult *din Torah*, but I simply do not have the time to devote to it. Could you take it upon yourself?"

R' David agreed. The next day two men came before him and outlined their case. Each person carefully explained his side of the story, while R' David listened thoughtfully. When the time came, he passed his ruling in favor of one of them and the two paid him the court fee. The next time he saw R' Chaim, he told him all about the case and how he had ruled.

R' Chaim smiled and said kindly, "My friend, do you realize that the case you judged is very similar to the case which you brought before me? Think a moment, did you not handle your case just like I handled the one in which you were personally involved?! Surely, you must realize that it was your own personal connection that made you blind to the truth then, for when you had to look at the facts objectively now, you saw the matter in its proper light!"

R' David realized that this was absolutely true and nodded. He thanked R' Chaim heartily for having opened his eyes.

Time passed. One day one of the men involved in R' David's case happened to visit Novardok and went to pay his respects to the rabbi, R' David.

After exchanging pleasantries, R' David asked him, "And what happened as a final result of the case that I judged for you?"

The visitor smiled and said, "There never was such a case! I never had an argument with that other man. It was all R' Chaim's doing. He put us up to it. He told each of us what to say and even gave us the money to pay for the court hearing."

R' David finally understood the lengths to which R' Chaim had gone to make him see the justification of his ruling. He exclaimed in amazement, "I thought that I knew R' Chaim, that I was able to appreciate his greatness. But, now, I see that he is far greater than I ever dreamed. I also understand why he is regarded as the *gadol hador*, the leader of his generation!"

The Magic Touch

"אֶצֹּק רוּחִי עַל זַרְעֶךָ"

I will pour of My spirit upon your seed
(Haftorah Parashas Vayikra, Yeshaya 44:3)

There was a certain energy that radiated from the Shpoli Zeide, a certain fervor and enthusiasm that accompanied all of his actions. With every single motion of his hand or finger, a spiritual energy burned and glowed purely for the sake of heaven, to cause pleasure to his Creator. This, perhaps, is what put the chasidim so in awe of their Rebbe.

When the Shpoli Zeide once visited R' Shneur Zalman of Liady, the Lubavitcher Rebbe asked him, "Tell me, where do you derive your special power? What is the source of your limitless energy and holy enthusiasm which constantly pour forth from you?"

The Shpoli Zeide replied: "When I was a child of three, I was taken to the saintly Baal Shem Tov. I looked into his face and was struck by the sublime glow that rested upon it. Not only that, the Rebbe actually placed his holy hand upon my heart. And from that time on, I have felt a certain warmth enveloping all of my limbs, lending them a special energy and strength. It is this warmth that is the wellspring of my enthusiasm."

"You see," he explained, "the slightest motion or movement of a *tzaddik* like the Baal Shem Tov can exert its influence for years, even for an entire lifetime!"

Parental Merit

"אֶצֹק רוּחִי עַל זַרְעֶךָ וּבִרְכָתִי עַל צֶאֱצָאֶיךָ"

*I will pour of My spirit upon your seed and My blessing upon
your descendants*
(Haftorah Parashas Vayikra, Yeshaya 44:3)

The two great scholars had just finished their morning prayers and not having seen each other for a long time, allowed themselves a short conversation before breakfast. R' Naftali of Ropshitz began speaking about his family lineage; he mentioned his father and grandfather and enumerated the famous scholars in his family tree that led back all the way to the *Shelah Hakadosh*, the famous R' Yeshaya Horowitz.

R' Feivel of Zavrez, a noted scholar in his own right, could not boast of such a line of learned and famous men and was disturbed by R' Naftali's words.

"I don't understand," he began. "After such a fervent *tefillah*, such deep concentration, such fiery devotion, do you still feel it necessary to enumerate your family tree and all the illustrious sages who are your ancestors?"

R' Naftali explained, "Yes, indeed. When I have finished praying that is precisely the time when I must remind myself of who my ancestors were. Let me explain. You rise at midnight, say the *tikkun chatzos* and then continue studying until dawn. Then you begin preparing yourself for the morning prayers, carefully, purifying all your thoughts, reciting first some *Tehillim* and giving charity to the poor. You study *mishnayos* until the time for the morning prayers arrives. Then, these are recited with deep concentration and fervor; you pronounce each word clearly, with awe and reverence.

"And when you have finished, you cannot help feeling good. You have accomplished something valuable. The prayers you have just offered up to your Creator are far beyond any of the prayers which your father or grandfather uttered for they were simple, G-d-fearing people. They knew nothing of holy *kavanos* and the like. Am I not right, R' Feivel?

"As for me, I too rise at midnight, go through the *tikkun chatzos* just like you. I also remain awake, studying, for the remainder of the night. I also take my time and care in preparing for my morning prayers. I focus all my thoughts in pure concentration upon the *tefillah* and finally, when I finish, I am exhausted from the emotional effort, just like you.

"But there is a difference. At this point, when I begin to feel pleased with myself, I think, 'Reb Naftali, do you really think that you *davened* as you should have? Do you think that you *davened* like your great ancestors did? Think of who they were! Men like *Shelah Hakadosh*! Can you begin to compare your worship of G-d to theirs?!' When I begin to think about it, I see that I do not even reach up to their ankles! And so, when I have finished praying, I cannot allow myself to become smug. I must think back to my ancestry for then I see that my accomplishment is nothing as compared to theirs!"

The Shach's Daughter

"אֶצָּק רוּחִי עַל זַרְעֶךָ וּבִרְכָתִי עַל צֶאֱצָאֶיךָ: וְצָמְחוּ בְּבֵין חָצִיר"

I will pour of My spirit upon Your seed and My blessing upon
your descendants
(Haftorah Parashas Vayikra, Yeshaya 44:4)

War was raging between Austria and France. The French forces captured the city where R' Shabsai Hakohen, the Shach, lived. They ran riot through the streets — sacking, plundering, murdering even women and children in cold blood. When they burst into the Shach's house in the Jewish quarter, his wife collapsed and died of fright. The Shach quickly placed his five-year-old daughter on his shoulders, snatched back some of his valuables from the soldiers and fled for his life.

He ran towards the forest which lay on the outskirts of the city. But there in the middle of the forest, R' Shabsai encountered another unit of soldiers. In his fright, he ran wherever his feet carried him, unaware that his little daughter had fallen.

Abandoned in the middle of the forest, the little girl first whimpered, then wept. The soldiers, with the king at their head, drew near, discovered the small bundle and took pity on her. The king ordered that the little girl be brought to the safety of his coach. There she was calmed and as soon as she stopped crying, the king ordered a meal set before her. She refused to touch a thing.

"Why don't you eat, little girl?" he asked gently.

"I am Jewish," she explained candidly in a clear childish voice, "and am not permitted to eat your food." The king did not force her but had some fruits brought to satisfy her hunger.

The little girl had a charm and beauty that captivated the king. He decided to take her home to the palace to be a companion for his only daughter, the princess.

The two girls were the same age. Soon they became inseparable friends. They did everything together and were alike in every way except one — the Jewish girl firmly refused to eat food that was not kosher. And surprisingly, she knew exactly what was permitted and what was forbidden.

Time went by and their fondness for one another grew. One night the Jewish girl awoke in a fright. Looking around, she noticed a large snake coiled around the princess' neck. "Help!" she shouted hysterically. "Help! A snake! A snake is choking the princess!"

Fear made her voice travel to the far corners of the palace. The servants, the guards and the king himself came rushing. They killed the snake just in time. The princess' life was saved!

The king and queen were overjoyed. The Jewish girl, the forest foundling, became a heroine. More than ever she became a palace favorite, not only for her charming, sweet ways, but, also, for the role she had played in saving the princess' life.

When they were a little older, the king decided that it was time to begin the girls' formal education and a special tutor was brought to the palace. One day, the tutor noticed that the rabbi's daughter left the food, which had been brought, untouched. "You ungrateful girl," he scolded, "Is this food not good enough for you? Is your appetite more spoiled and pampered than that of a princess?!"

The Jewish girl was deeply hurt and burst into tears.

Her sensitive heart was offended. That evening, at dinner, the princess told the king what had happened. The king was vexed and summoned the tutor. He upbraided him for having upset the princess' companion and made him promise never to insult her in any way again.

And so the years passed, pleasantly, uneventfully. The two girls grew up, their friendship growing with the years until they reached their twelfth year.

It was a foggy night. All was dark when suddenly, streaks of brilliant light lit up the sky. A fire had broken out in the palace. The Shach's daughter awoke; panic-stricken by the billowing, choking smoke, she reached the window, jumped out and landed lightly on her feet.

She ran and ran until she had left the city behind her and found herself in a wilderness. Suddenly, she felt herself seized by strong arms. She looked up and saw fierce, scarred, terrifying faces all around her. She had run right into a robber's den; she was now their prisoner.

"What are we going to do with this child?" the robber chief asked himself. Boldly, the young Jewish girl spoke up, "Why don't you take me to the city and sell me as a slave."

This idea struck the bandit as excellent. The following day he traveled with her to the marketplace of a distant city. The Jewish community heard that a captive Jewish girl was being held up for sale and was determined to ransom her. But the robber demanded an exorbitant price — five hundred gold pieces!

Jews always tried to fulfill the mitzvah to redeem captives at any price. And indeed, this time, too, a good, wealthy man stepped forward and offered to pay the entire sum himself. And so the Shach's daughter returned to her people and was raised in the home of this wealthy Jew.

The years passed and she grew up into a fine young girl of marriageable age who so pleased her Jewish master that he decided to marry her off to his own son.

Some more time passed and the Jewish community was threatened by troubles. A high-ranking officer had come to the city with written permission from the king empowering him to do whatever he wished to the Jewish community. He demanded a huge sum of money.

The Jews were beside themselves with fear. "Even if we sell all of our possessions to pay this fine, we will not cover half of the sum demanded of us!" they wept. They sent a special delegation to the officer, begging for leniency, but he hardheartedly refused. "All Jews have money," he said. "Everyone knows that!"

The Jews gathered in their *batei knesses* and prayed to *Hashem* to repeal the harsh decree.

That night the young husband returned home to his wife, the Shach's daughter, looking very unhappy. When she asked him what troubled him, he told her everything.

Upon hearing the tale of woe, the young woman said, "I know many languages. I can write well. Perhaps if I wrote a letter to the king explaining the difficult situation of the Jewish community he might have pity on us."

The young man was doubtful. "I don't think it would make the slightest difference. This officer, who bears the letter of decree, is none other than the princess' husband! That gives him almost unlimited power!"

He expected that this information would dampen his wife's hopes, but was surprised to see her react with joy. Was that princess not the very one with whom she had grown up, whose life she had once saved?!

She did not divulge this to her husband, but said, "I know. I will not bother with a letter to the king but will go in person to visit the officer's wife. With *Hashem's* help, I will be able to help our people."

On the following morning, the Shach's daughter, dressed in her finest clothes, went to the princess' home, pretending that she was an expert seamstress. The latter was overjoyed at the prospect of having a skilled seamstress and invited her in. Their conversation covered a variety of subjects until suddenly the 'seamstress' said, "Don't you recognize me? Don't you remember who I am?" She waited for a reply.

The young princess looked hard, but shook her head. How should she know a common seamstress?

The Jewish woman now revealed her identity. "I am the young Jewish girl whom your father, the king, found in the forest. I grew up together with you in the palace. On the night of the great fire I jumped out of the window and ran for my life, but was captured by highwaymen."

At first the princess refused to believe her. But, as she examined the woman's face closely, she recognized the familiar fine lines and detected the gentle character reflected in those noble features. She became excited and clasped the woman in a fond embrace.

"Tell me all about yourself! Tell me, what happened to you after that terrible fire? We were sure that you were burned to death since the entire wing was reduced to cinders. Nothing recognizable remained. How we mourned your death, my father, mother and I! And here you are, alive! Safe and sound! How happy I am to see you well!"

The Shach's daughter related how she had been

captured and sold in a distant city, how she had been bought by a Jewish man and raised in his home.

"I live here now. I married my master's son and live in the midst of the Jewish community."

She took a deep breath and continued, "That is the reason why I came. You see, our people are in grave danger."

"Tell me, what is the matter? What can I do to help you?"

"Your husband imposed an enormous fine upon the Jewish community, a fine which is above and beyond our means. He says that if we do not pay it, which we know we cannot, he will send his soldiers to seize our property by force. They will riot through the Jewish quarter and will not stop, even at murder. You are the only one who can help us. You must speak to him."

"I alone will not be able to convince him. You must come with me and represent your people. Let us go together to his suite and see what we can accomplish."

The Jewish woman nodded. The two went to the officer's rooms. He was surprised to see his wife together with a strange woman and asked what they wanted. The Jewish woman explained the purpose of her visit. He listened, a cold expression on his face. He was unmoved. He loved his wife and tried to please her, but, when it came to money, he was a harsh, difficult person.

Suddenly the Jewish woman had an idea. "Why don't you inform the king that I am alive and did not perish in the great fire, as he suspected? If he hears that, he will be overjoyed and will send you great gifts."

It was just as she had predicted. The officer agreed to send a letter to the king with the news that the princess' childhood friend, the forest foundling, was still alive and living in his city. The king was so glad to hear this that he rewarded him with many costly gifts, worth more than the sum he had demanded from the Jewish community. And so, thanks to the Shach's daughter, the harsh decree was abolished and the Jewish community breathed a sigh of relief.

Two years passed. One Friday a rabbi arrived in the city and was asked to speak on *Shabbos*. Everyone gathered to hear him for he was a famous scholar. Even the women's gallery in the synagogue was filled to the rafters.

People listened spellbound to his moving speech and among them our heroine. Where had she heard that voice before? It was so familiar yet buried so deep in her memory! She let her mind travel back into the past, into the far distant past, when she had been a very little girl. Could it be? Could this be the voice of her long-lost father?!

When she returned home she did not say a word. She did not want to make a fool of herself. Instead she asked her husband to invite the visiting rabbi to their house for a meal.

The rabbi accepted. During the meal they touched on all kinds of subjects. The rabbi happened to mention that he had once had a small daughter who had gotten lost in the forest when he had run away from the invading French armies. "She was only five years old at the time, poor thing," he said, tears forming in his eyes. "She disappeared and to this day, I do not know what became of her. Either she died in the forest or was captured by the enemy."

The young woman no longer had any doubts that this was her father! She jumped up and cried,

"Father! Father! I am your lost daughter. I am the child lost in the forest!"

When the townspeople learned of the wonderful reunion, they were very happy, but not surprised. "After all, even as a young girl she carefully kept *kashrus* even in the king's palace," they said. "She was always careful not to let anything forbidden pass her lips. Thus, she was thought worthy to be redeemed by the rich Jew and grew up to marry his son. She was, truly, her father's daughter."

פָּרָשַׁת צַו

Parashas Tzav

Money, Yes? Shechitah, No?

"צַו אֶת אַהֲרֹן"

Command Aharon (6:2)

This command also urges. Special urging is necessary
wherever financial expense is involved.

(Rashi)

R' Yisrael Salanter once stopped in an inn during his
travels. The Jewish innkeeper was very impressed
by his distinguished appearance, his flowing beard and
stately bearing, and even before greeting him, asked,

"Are you perhaps a *shochet*? I have an animal to
slaughter. It is very difficult for me to transport it all the
way to town and back. I thought perhaps you could save
me the trip by slaughtering it for me."

R' Yisrael sat at his table. A few minutes later, he
turned to the innkeeper and asked, "Would you perhaps
have a ruble to lend me?"

"I would lend you a ruble but I don't even know you,"
said the innkeeper. "How do I know that you would
return it to me?"

R' Yisrael's eyes glinted with indignation. "You are not
ready to trust me for one single ruble, yet, only a
moment ago, even before greeting me and asking my

name, you were willing to trust me with slaughtering an animal, a *mitzvah* about which the Torah cautions us so carefully, a commandment which only experts can perform after years of study and practice."

As Long as They Still Sacrifice

"וּשְׁמַרְתֶּם אֶת מִשְׁמֶרֶת ה' וְלֹא תָמוּתוּ"
And you shall keep the charge of Hashem and you will not die (8:35)

The second *Beis Hamikdash* stood for four hundred and twenty years. During its final years the Romans sent mighty armies to capture the land and destroy the *Beis Hamikdash*, but were unsuccessful.

The Romans fought against the Jews for three years. They besieged Jerusalem and tried to penetrate the wall that encircled the city. They brought huge battering rams and catapults that hurled heavy boulders at the wall. But all in vain. In the fourth year, the Roman emperor sent even more forces, this time headed by a famous general, Titus, may his name be erased.

Titus arrived in Jerusalem with his reinforcements in the month of *Nisan*. Slowly the armies approached the city. Titus was certain that his weapons and soldiers

would prevail against the stubborn stronghold of Jerusalem. But try as he might, he could not breach the wall.

As long as the daily sacrifices were brought, the Romans were helpless. When all of the animals inside the city walls had been used for sacrifices, or for food, the Jews bought others from the Roman soldiers. Each day, they would lower two chests full of gold over the side of the wall. The soldiers would empty out the gold and put two sheep into the chests instead. The Jews would then haul up the chests and take the two sheep for the daily sacrifice, one in the morning and one at night.

On the seventeenth of *Tammuz*, however, something terrible happened. The Jews lowered the chests with gold, expecting two sheep in return. This time, however, the Romans tricked them and instead of sheep, they put two *pigs* into the chests. And as soon as these impure animals set their hoofs to the wall, the entire country trembled and quaked!

On that infamous day, the daily *tamid* sacrifice ceased to be offered. And when that stopped the Romans were able to breach the wall of Jerusalem. Finally, on the ninth of Av, they succeeded in setting fire to the *Beis Hamikdash*.

(*Yerushalmi* Tractate *Berachos 4:1*)

Wisdom — To What Purpose?

"אַל יִתְהַלֵּל חָכָם בְּחָכְמָתוֹ"

Let not the wise man glory in his wisdom
(Haftorah Parashas Tzav Yirmiyah 9:22)

Shimon and Shmuel grew up together. As little boys, they roamed the village streets, playing with carefree abandon, as boys will. When they grew a bit older they went to *cheder* together, sharing one school bench and sometimes even one *gemara*.

Outwardly, they may have appeared to be alike, but they were very different. Shimon was an average student who grew up to be a very average person with no outstanding qualities. Shmuel, however, was gifted with a keen mind. Everything he learned remained fixed in his memory and, as he gained more knowledge, he was able to understand more and more. Aside from his natural cleverness, he was a good-natured person, always willing to do a favor for another.

The two grew up and as chance would have it, the clever lad married the daughter of a poor man while Shimon, the average youth, married the daughter of a wealthy man; both brides came from the same city. And so the two childhood companions went to settle there in their wives' hometown.

By the nature of things, Shmuel, who had once been respected for his fine mind and good deeds, was now a nobody, the son-in-law of a pauper. It was Shimon, the simple fellow, who sat up front in the *beis knesses* at the eastern wall, alongside his rich father-in-law; Shimon who received the important *aliyos*; Shimon whom people greeted on the street and with whom they shook hands. Shmuel was pushed aside and ignored.

Shmuel felt the neglect deeply. In his heart he knew that he was far more deserving than his childhood friend. People did not give him a chance. They only looked for superficial values, for money and prestige. No one knew what a scholar Shmuel was! No one knew what a fine fellow he was! It was very painful.

Just at this time, everyone began speaking about a famous Rav, the Sanzer Rebbe, R' Chaim.

"This is my chance," Shmuel thought. "Finally, I can gain the recognition I truly deserve. But first I must convince Shimon to join me in visiting the Sanzer Rebbe. Once we are there, everyone will see who measures up and who doesn't. The Sanzer Rebbe will not be fooled. He will know that I am the scholar, the fine fellow, while Shimon only rests upon his father-in-law's reputation and is not very special."

It took some convincing, but in the end, not only did Shimon agree to visit the Sanzer Rebbe, even his wealthy father-in-law agreed to come along.

The trip was long and tiring, but Shmuel did not mind. He kept imagining all the honor that would be his when the Rebbe merely looked at him with his keen eyes and recognized him for what he really was.

But Shmuel was in for a shocking disappointment. For, even in Sanz, nothing changed. It was the rich man and his son-in-law who entered first to greet the Rebbe. The Rebbe remained closeted with them for a long time. Later, the rich man and his son-in-law were seated near the Rebbe, at the head of the table; they were called up to the Torah. Poor Shmuel was relegated to the back, ignored. Even when he went in to the Rebbe, after a long wait, the latter did not acknowledge him. R' Chaim returned his "Shalom Aleichem Rebbe," with an "Aleichem Shalom", but dismissed him at once; he paid no special attention to him as he had to the wealthy pair.

Shmuel was disillusioned, crushed with disappointment. Didn't the Rebbe, at least, see what a fine man he was, what a clever scholar and good fellow he was? Why did he ignore him? Was there no truth in this world? Was everything a sham, a superficial, outward show?

The first *Shabbos* meal passed. Shmuel had been expecting the Rebbe to single him out any minute, to ask him to say something, to honor him with a *l'chaim* toast. But nothing. It was as if he did not exist.

Shmuel bided his time. There was another meal and then another. But there was no sign from the Rebbe, no acknowledgement. He was a nobody. Finally, at *shalosh seudos*, his patience burst.

"I can bear this no longer," he thought, rushing out of the room. No one took note of his leave, but he didn't care any more. "If there is no truth even here, by the far-sighted, all-knowing Rebbe, then it is really time for *Mashiach* to come!" he muttered bitterly.

Shabbos passed and it came time to say *havdalah*. Shmuel could not wait to return home. He had had enough of obscurity. He wanted to get away from this place as fast as possible.

But he had a surprise waiting for him. Right after *havdalah* the *gabbai*, who had ignored him all *Shabbos*, came up to him and said, "The Rebbe would like to see you in his study."

His heart pounding with excitement and one final hope, Shmuel entered. R' Chaim gave him a piercing look and said, "Our people have been in exile for two thousand years. For two thousand years, ever since the *Beis Hamikdash* was destroyed, they have been praying for redemption, for *Mashiach*. Not only do we pray, even the angels in heaven pray for the ultimate *geulah* — redemption — for our people. Yet there are evil forces who prosecute against the Jews and ask, 'Why do the Jews really need this redemption? Do they sincerely want it? Who is it who prays for salvation? Only those with personal problems — those who fail in business, those with enemies, with hard luck, those who are sick. They pray only for their own selfish reasons.' That is the reason why our nation still suffers in exile!

"This *Shabbos* happened to be a favorable time in heaven, a time of good-will. Our people were only a hairsbreadth away from the real *geulah* when, suddenly, a plaintiff angel spoke up and asked, 'Are they really eager for redemption? Do they really want it and need it?' And then he continued, 'Look at the learned Jew on earth, Shmuel. He has devoted his entire life to the study of Torah and good neighborly deeds, so that he might gain recognition and honor! He sees his friend getting recognition which he thinks is undeserved. He sees his friend succeeding in life and begrudges him his popularity. That is why he prays for *Mashiach* to come, so that he can be honored instead of his friend.'"

The Rebbe looked pointedly at Shmuel and continued, "You, with your petty desires, caused the *geulah* to be delayed!"

Shmuel turned ashen and burst into tears. These tears washed away the crookedness in his mind, for he, suddenly, saw things in their true light. He, suddenly, realized that the Rebbe had seen straight through him, had seen the truth which, even he, himself, had not been willing to admit. All these years he had been studying Torah, not for its sake, but for his own sake, for his honor! That is what had brought him here to the Rebbe. But the Rebbe had seen the truth! And the Rebbe had told him that he had held up the *geulah*...

Shmuel wept long and bitterly. He saw man's true purpose on this world. From now on he would not be guided by selfish motives. He would strive for the good of his people! He would fulfill his goal on this world, not for himself but for the sake of his people!

The Chasidim Who Chose Poverty

"אַל יִתְהַלֵּל עָשִׁיר בְּעָשְׁרוֹ, כִּי אִם בְּזֹאת יִתְהַלֵּל הַמִּתְהַלֵּל הַשְׂכֵּל וְיָדֹעַ אוֹתִי"

Let the rich man not glory in his riches... only in this shall he that glories, glory, in wisely knowing Me
(Haftorah Parashas Tzav, Yirmiya 9:22,23)

Most of the chasidim of R' Uri of Sterlisk had one thing in common. They were poverty-stricken. And yet, strangely enough, when they came to visit the Rebbe and pour out their woes before him, making their personal requests, they never asked for riches. They never asked the Rebbe to pray for their livelihood — *parnasah* and material welfare. The *Saraf's* chasidim paid no attention to worldly matters. They were concerned only with the worship of G-d and the fulfillment of *mitzvos*.

Others would note this in amazement. Once, consumed by curiosity, a visiting Admor confronted R' Uri with the following question, "Why is it, R' Uri, that most of your followers are so desperately poor?"

R' Uri smiled, "That is a matter of choice, not chance. They prefer poverty over riches, for, thus, they are more detached from the vanities of this world."

While he was talking a chasid happened to pass by. R' Uri called to him from the window, asking him to come inside. When he had entered, R' Uri turned to him and said, "You see that I have a distinguished guest here with me today. This is the perfect opportunity for you to make a request. Our combined prayers will help you get your heart's desire. What is it that you wish for yourself and your family?"

Without hesitation, the chasid spoke, his voice choked with emotion, "My most fervent wish is that I be privileged to recite the *baruch she'amar* prayer each morning with the same fervor and holy absorption as the Rebbe himself."

The Worthless Assistant

"וְאַל יִתְהַלֵּל הַגִּבּוֹר בִּגְבוּרָתוֹ... כִּי אִם בְּזֹאת יִתְהַלֵּל הַמִּתְהַלֵּל
הַשְׂכֵּל וְיָדֹעַ אוֹתִי"

*Let the rich man not glory in his riches... only in this shall he
that glories, glory, in wisely knowing Me
(Haftorah Parashas Tzav, Yirmiyahu 9:22,23)*

As a young man, R' Yosef Dov Soloveitchik, later
the Rav of Brisk, wished to meet R' Shlomo
Kluger, the rabbi of Brody and *gadol hador*, and make his
acquaintance.

The journey from Lithuania all the way to Brody in
Galicia, was long and expensive, far beyond the purse of
R' Yosef Dov. Since he could not afford to travel as a
passenger, he hired himself out as a wagoner's assistant.
The driver needed someone to accompany him on the
long, long trip; he welcomed the offer.

Everything was fine until the young scholar took a
turn at the reins. Sensing a new, inexperienced, driver,
the horses bolted. They galloped full speed ahead. The
wagon and its passengers pitched from side to side. When
the wagoner had regained control of the horses, he
turned furiously on his assistant, "Don't you know the
first thing about horses? Don't you even have enough
sense to hold on to the reins, you good-for-nothing?"
And, for good measure, he gave R' Yosef Dov a number
of resounding blows.

At long last, the journey was over; they had reached
Brody. And when R' Yosef Dov parted from his
employer, the wagoner barely said good-bye. He was glad
to be rid of his worthless assistant.

R' Yosef Dov made his way at once to the home of R' Shlomo Kluger where a different welcome awaited him. The young man's reputation had gone before him. The more R' Shlomo Kluger spoke with him, the more impressed he became and he begged the young *gaon* to honor the people of Brody with a *drashah* that *Shabbos*.

The news flew through the city. All of Brody gathered in the *beis knesses* to hear the genius from Lithuania speak. And the wagoner was present, too.

When R' Yosef Dov walked up to the platform, the wagoner nearly fainted. He recognized the inefficient young helper who had earned his ire on the long trip. He remembered how he had scolded him, shouted at him, even struck him! He grew alternately flushed and pale with self-embarrassment as he recalled his behavior.

He trembled like a leaf throughout the *drashah*. After an eternity, when it was finally over, the wagoner dragged himself up to the front of the synagogue and threw himself at R' Yosef Dov's feet, weeping, "Rebbe, forgive me!"

"You have nothing to feel bad about, my dear man," R' Yosef Dov comforted him. "Had you scolded me about my Torah scholarship, had you struck me for being an *am haaretz*, you would, perhaps, have been guilty of disrespect for the Torah. But you rebuked me for being a poor driver. On that account, you were perfectly justified. In truth, I know nothing about horses."

The Unforgotten Favor

"אַל יִתְהַלֵּל עָשִׁיר בְּעָשְׁרוֹ... כִּי אֲנִי ה' עֹשֶׂה חֶסֶד
מִשְׁפָּט וּצְדָקָה"

Let the rich man not glory in his riches... for I am Hashem Who
does kindness, justice and righteousness
(Haftorah Parashas Tzav, Yirmiya 9:23)

It is a long way from Lelov to Lizensk. Not a distance that one would consider traveling by foot! But R' David, who could not afford to ride by coach, once decided to walk that long way when he wished to visit his Rebbe, R' Elimelech.

While on the road, R' David noticed an approaching coach. When the coach drew alongside, he saw that the passenger was a wealthy chasid from Warsaw.

"Where are you headed, Reb Yid?" asked R' David.

"I am going to Lizensk, to visit R' Elimelech," replied the wealthy man.

"Can you perhaps take me along?"

Somewhat reluctantly, the rich man said, "All right, up with you, but make sure to shake the dust off your feet first. I don't want my coach all dirtied."

R' David shook himself clean and climbed on. Throughout the trip he was subjected to rude remarks, but he listened in silence, not deigning to reply. He realized that his host had mistaken him for one of the many traveling beggars.

When they arrived, to the rich man's surprise, it was his passenger, the shabby 'beggar' who was admitted first to the Rebbe. As he sat outside the Rebbe's study, waiting, he mulled things over, finally realizing that the poor Jew who had been his traveling companion was no simple beggar. As the minutes dragged by and became hours, the rich man felt pangs of conscience assailing him. Surely, this must have been a great man, perhaps even a *tzaddik nistar*. The words of ridicule came back to him and he felt thoroughly ashamed.

"When he comes out," thought the rich man, "I will offer him a ride all the way back to Lelov. Then I will try to make up for my disgraceful behavior."

Two hours later R' David, finally, emerged. The rich man jumped to his feet. He wished to offer him a ride home as soon as he had finished speaking to the Rebbe.

R' David knew exactly what he wanted to say and before he could open his mouth, said, "I must remain here for some time still, and cannot return with you. But I wish to pass on some important advice. Keep your ears open on the way back. When you hear cries of distress, follow them up. You will know what to do afterwards, I am sure."

The rich man was now certain that his passenger was no simple man. And so, as he traveled home, he was alert to every sound.

The horses sped more quickly than usual; they seemed to know exactly where they were headed. He hardly needed to guide them at all; the coach wheels seemed to fly as if freshly greased. The rich man had gone half way, in a very short time, when, suddenly, there was a piercing cry from a thick nearby forest. Someone was calling for help in Polish.

The Jew from Warsaw tugged at the reins and the horses were off the road, pulling in the direction of the cries. The going was more difficult now. The cries were getting louder and more desperate.

Suddenly he saw it. Looming up from the shadows was a magnificent coach hitched up to two horses already half sunk in a bed of quicksand. The terrified horses thrashed about, causing the coach to sink more quickly. Trapped inside was a Polish nobleman, screaming for help in desperation.

Without hesitation, the Jew tied one end of a stout rope to the back of the sinking coach, the other end to his own carriage. He whipped his horses again and again. Panting and pulling, pawing and straining, they drew forth the coach. With a huge sucking noise the quicksand gave up its prize; the gentile's coach stood on firm ground.

The Jew went over to the door and pulled it open. The poor nobleman inside was a sorry sight, all muddy, white and speechless, trembling from shock and cold.

"Where do you live?" the Jew asked. He lived in Warsaw, which made things easier. Cleaning him off as best he could, the Jew took him inside his own carriage and drove on.

It was late at night when they arrived. The Jew went directly to his home where he ordered his servants to bathe and feed the stranger and put him in a fresh, warm bed. On the morrow he was a new man.

The nobleman thanked his rescuer-and-host profusely and went on to his own home. A few days later, the Jew received a card asking him to come to the offices of the Polish nobleman. He went, but, when the nobleman offered him a generous reward, he turned it down emphatically and said, "I only did my duty as a human being and a Jew! I do not deserve any prize for that!" The nobleman was impressed, but insisted in writing down his name for future reference. "You may need my services some time in the future. I will never forget that you saved my life."

Much water passed under the bridge of time. The wheel of fortune made many revolutions, taking down our Warsaw Jew, who had been up on top. His business failed, causing him to sell all of his property, until he was left with no more than a suit of shabby clothing upon his back — and nothing in his pocket. He was reduced to begging from door to door. He wandered from city to city, town to town, begging for his bread, fortunate, if he could put some food into his mouth each day.

He lived thus for ten whole years. By that time, he had become so accustomed to this way of life that he had forgotten that things had ever been different. At least the passing time had been kind in helping him forget.

Thus it was, that when his erratic travels brought him again to Warsaw, he had no special memories of that place. Nor did he feel embarrassed to walk the city streets, his hand stretched out for alms. And if he saw a rich man approaching, he did not turn his head in shame. On the contrary, he hurried forward, hoping to arouse that man's compassion and earn his day's bread. This is how he came to step up to a luxurious coach and beg its master for charity.

The man inside looked at the beggar outside. The face was familiar. Wait! Now he remembered. Could it be?! Could this be the same rich Warsaw Jew in whose magnificent home he had spent a night?!

The Jew, now, took notice of the gentile's studied interest and grew afraid. Did the nobleman intend to call the police? He lifted his heels and ran.

"Hey, there, you Jew! Wait! Come here!"

The Jew ran even faster. The nobleman ordered his footman to pursue the fleeing beggar and bring him back. The half-starved Jew was no match for the well-fed servant. In minutes he was standing before the Polish nobleman. This time their roles were reversed; it was he who was pale and trembling.

The nobleman reassured him. "I mean you no harm! I just wanted to know your name. You look so familiar to me."

The Jew shrugged his shoulders in surprise. Best to humor him, he thought, and told the man his name.

"But I do know you!" said the man inside the coach. "And you should know me too! Does quicksand have any significance to you? Does a sinking coach not strike a bell in your memory?"

Suddenly, it all came back to him. This was the man whom he had once saved. He nodded in affirmation.

The nobleman looked at him from head to toe and asked, "How did you end up like this? What happened to your riches?"

The Jew shook his head sadly and told him his tale of woe. "At first I purposely forgot everything," he said in conclusion, "but, now, even when I try, I find it difficult to remember anything. It is better that way." The nobleman looked at him sadly, sorry to hear the forgotten tale.

"I cannot let you remain thus. You saved my life! Here, take these two thousand rubles and rehabilitate yourself. Find yourself some lodgings and invest in business. You can return to your former position of wealth if you show the proper will."

Revived and encouraged, the Jew opened a new page in his book of life and soon regained the wealth and prestige he had once possessed.

Many years had passed, since that fateful day in the forest. Since then, R' Elimelech had passed on to the world of truth and R' David of Lelov, a once obscure chasid, had become a leader of repute. The Warsaw Jew still had no idea who his onetime passenger had been.

When he went to pay the *gadol hador*, the Lelover Rebbe, a visit, he did not recognize his former beggar-passenger, but R' David did remember him.

"Tell me about yourself," the great man said to his visitor. The Warsaw Jew began a brief autobiography of his life and the strange ups and downs which he had experienced. He concluded with the miraculous comeback which he had made, thanks to the nobleman's gift.

Throughout this amazing story, R' David sat, silently nodding. When the visitor had finished, he said, "Yes, I know. I know. I am the passenger whom you picked up outside of Lelov and took to R' Elimelech of Lizensk. You did not treat me courteously on that trip, but mocked and embarrassed me throughout. I knew that heaven had decided to punish you with death and, as soon as I arrived, I went to the Rebbe and asked what I could do to mitigate your sentence. Together, we reached some form of compromise on the heavenly decision. If you were to suffer abject poverty, that would in effect be a form of death, as our Sages have taught. Ten years of suffering through poverty would serve to atone for your sin."

"But why did that period terminate? Why was I restored to wealth, after those ten years?"

R' David smiled. "But you did do me a kindness! You gave me a ride all the way to Lizensk. We must not forget that! I wanted to return the favor. And I did, with the help of *Hashem*."

פָּרָשַׁת שְׁמִינִי

Parashas Shemini

Women to the Rescue

"וַיַּקְרִיבוּ לִפְנֵי ה' אֵשׁ זָרָה... וַתֵּצֵא אֵשׁ מִלִּפְנֵי ה'
וַתֹּאכַל אוֹתָם"

*And they brought near improper fire before Hashem... and a fire
went forth from before Hashem and consumed them (10:1,2)*

Τhe *Midrash* says that Aharon's two sons, Nadav and
Avihu, died because they never got married.

However, the Torah specifically says otherwise. They
died for having brought foreign fire to the holy altar.

How are we to reconcile these conflicting reasons?

The following story gives us an answer:

R' David'l of Zubeltov, son of the Admor, R'
Menachem Mendel of Kosov, once, became so ill that
even the best physicans despaired of his life.

Not so his wife. Pesya Leah, daughter of the eminent
Sassover Rebbe, refused to make peace with this
sentence. She sat by her husband's bedside and did not
cease her praying and weeping. "Please, *Hashem*," she
pleaded tearfully, "let my saintly husband recover."

The good woman's fervent prayer split the very
heavens and, despite the doctors' gloomy prognosis, the
patient began to improve slowly. Soon R' David'l was
back on his feet, leading his flock as before.

R' David'l knew to whom he owed his recovery. He knew of his wife's devoted prayers. Once, in the company of his closest chasidim, he said, "Now that I am well again, I understand what the *midrash* says. Nadav and Avihu died because they did not have wives. If they had had wives like my own worthy *Rebbetzin* Leah, who would have prayed for them, they would surely have been saved from death despite their having brought improper fire before *Hashem*."

The Wrong Conclusion

"יַיִן וְשֵׁכָר אַל־תֵּשְׁתְּ"
You shall not drink wine or liquor (10:9)

There was once a scholar of note who had the ill fortune of having a drunkard in the family who caused him no end of embarrassment. The drunkard would drink until he collapsed in the gutter. Street urchins would sling mud at him, poke him with sticks, mess up his clothing and ridicule him.

Each time he saw this, the *talmid chacham* would die a thousand deaths from shame and hurry away, as quickly as he could, so as not to be identified with his relative.

Once, when he saw his relative at his worst, the scholar decided that this must stop. When the drunk sobered up, the scholar offered to supply him with all the wine he needed on the condition that he drink it at home

and not make a public disgrace of himself and shame the family.

The scholar kept his cousin well stocked with wine and liquor at considerable expense. Still, he was spared the embarrassment of seeing the drunkard sprawled out on the pavement, the butt of every passerby.

Once, on his way to a wine shop, the scholar was caught in a sudden downpour. Within minutes the ground was flooded. Rain washed mud and dirt into the streets. Water flowed rapidly into already overflowing sewers. The scholar gingerly making his way through the streets, came upon a drunkard, lying in the gutter. Some young boys had already discovered him and were splattering him with mud, and filling his mouth with dirt. As soon as he saw this terrible sight, the scholar thought of his cousin.

"I must show him this man," he thought. "This picture of a drunk may cure him of his drunkenness altogether." He rushed home to fetch his relative.

When the drunkard beheld the lolling, begrimed figure, he bent over the man and whispered in his ear, "Tell me, where did you get liquor so strong as to make you this drunk?"

The scholar was furious! His plan had backfired. "Was this my purpose in bringing you here?" he asked in dismay and anger. "I hoped to cure you by showing you how disgusting this man looks. And instead, all you can think of is the liquor that made him drunk!"

(According to Midrash Tanchuma, Parashas Shemini 11)

Not By Messenger

"יַיִן וְשֵׁכָר אַל־תֵּשְׁתְּ"

You shall not drink wine or liquor (10:9)

He was a disgrace to his family, to his city and to his Rebbe. A Ruzhiner chasid in Sanok had begun drinking heavily and his family did not know what to do. They begged and pleaded with him to stop, but to no avail. The man had already acquired the bad habit and could not — would not — shake it off.

When the Rebbe heard of the terrible disgrace, he sent an express messenger to his chasid, telling him to come to Ruzhin at once. The drunkard did not dare refuse.

To his surprise, the Rebbe did not rebuke him angrily, but spoke softly, in a kindly, fatherly manner, making him feel ashamed of himself. He pointed out that he was not only hurting his family and embarrassing his fellow townspeople, but that he was causing a public *chillul Hashem*. The man bowed his head, realizing that all this was true. He felt ashamed.

But the Rebbe would not let him leave on this note. He grasped the chasid's hand warmly and made him promise to do his utmost to break the habit.

"From now on," the man vowed, "I will drink wine only for *kiddush* and *havdalah*!"

Before leaving, the chasid said, "I have one question to ask of the Rebbe. Why did you send a messenger to fetch me? You could have sent a messenger telling me to stop drinking. Why did you want to see me personally?"

"That is a very good question. I took my example from

the Torah, you see. In *parashas Shemini* Aharon Hakohen is given only one commandment directly — that of not drinking wine or liquor. Many other commandments apply to him, but they were explained through a messenger, his brother, Moshe.

"When a person is directed to abstain from drinking wine, he must be told this in person, face to face, not by way of a messenger."

Black Coffee

"הַגָּמָל... טָמֵא הוּא לָכֶם"
The camel...is impure for you (11:4)

The yearly fair was taking place in the big city. The fairgrounds were filled with makeshift stands and tables, which hardly left room for the hundreds of buyers and sellers, who had come to make a quick penny. Wares of all kinds and colors were brilliantly displayed and the customers passed from stand to stand seeking bargains. They had to shout to make themselves heard over the deafening din. The air throbbed with life and excitement.

Some people did their business on the fairgrounds themselves, others in nearby eating houses and the like. A group of Jewish merchants had gathered in a coffeehouse to see if they could make a mutual profit.

They had just settled down around a large table when a waiter came by to take their orders.

"What will you gentlemen have, please?" he asked, his pencil poised above a small pad.

"I'll have some coffee with milk," said one.

"Make that two."

"Three."

"Four."

The waiter looked around and counted, "Six coffees with milk." He noticed a seventh man who had not yet ordered. "And what will you have, sir?" he asked.

"I'll have my coffee black, if you don't mind," he replied quietly.

"Hey! What's this?! Are you on a diet?" the others laughed. "You can't really prefer black coffee to coffee with milk! And on an empty stomach, no less. Come on, join us. There is nothing like a really good cup of coffee first thing in the morning. Just what you need to help mellow you to make a good business deal."

Meanwhile the waiter had returned with their orders.

"Mmmmm. There is something special about this coffee today, don't you think?" one of them said. They all nodded in agreement. He now turned to the man with the black coffee and said, "Tell us, is their any special reason why you are drinking your coffee black today? I once visited your home and joined you in a cup of coffee with cream. You could not have eaten meat yet, could you?"

The men laughed, then looked at the seventh, waiting for his explanation. The latter lowered his eyes, as if ashamed, and said, "Perhaps, they have mixed some *treife* milk with the cow's milk."

"What!" all six pounced upon his words. "Did you not see the herd of healthy cows grazing in the back yard of this coffee house? What else would they be using but cow's milk! What a ridiculous presumption!"

Nevertheless, the seventh man continued sipping his black coffee, disregarding all the ridiculing remarks.

The waiter had been circulating among the other customers and could not help overhearing the word 'milk' repeated, over and over. He turned to their table and beamed, "I see that you are enjoying your morning coffee. It has a special flavor today, don't you think?" They nodded. "Shall I tell you why?" the waiter confided. "It is because this morning we mixed some camel's milk together with the cow's milk. This is a great delicacy, very rich and creamy. You can tell the difference, can't you?"

The six men turned pale. They had been so certain, so complacent, so convinced that they had been drinking kosher milk; yet, they had been mistaken after all and had committed a terrible sin! Only their companion, who had taken his coffee black, was spared that transgression. After begging forgiveness for having teased him, they said, "You must have had special heavenly protection to prevent you from sinning!"

"How does the verse go?" one of them added, "A *tzaddik* will come to no harm."

That *tzaddik* was **Simchah Bunim** the merchant, who later left business and became the famous **R' Simchah Bunim of Pshischa.**

The Kindly Stork

"וְאֵת הַחֲסִידָה"

And the stork (11:19)

R' Eliyahu Chaim Meisel, rabbi of Lodz, was a familiar figure to the rich congregants, as well as to the poor — he took from the rich and he gave to the poor. Even though the prosperous Jews did not resent his frequent requests and never refused their rabbi, they did feel complacent and smug about being so generous.

R' Eliyahu Chaim sensed this and was not happy about the situation.

And thus, he once said to them, "The Torah prohibits eating the stork, or *chasidah*, as she is called in Hebrew. Rashi explains that it is called *chasidah* because it does kindness, *chesed*, to its friends. But, if anything, being kind should make that bird permissible, not prohibited! Why then is the stork considered an impure fowl? The answer is that the *chasidah* assumes that by doing kindness it does more than is expected of it. Not at all! Kindness to one's fellows is not something praiseworthy and out of the ordinary; it is a natural duty."

Meat for Ten Coins

"וְהִתְקַדִּשְׁתֶּם וִהְיִיתֶם קְדשִׁים"

And you shall sanctify yourselves and you shall be holy (11:44)
And you should be holy — this refers to washing hands
before the meal

(Tractate Berachos 53b)

The Jews in *Eretz Yisrael* were under foreign rule. They were not free to keep the *mitzvos*, for their rulers passed laws forcing them to dress, act and eat just like they did. Thus, it was difficult to tell who was a Jew and who wasn't.

In those troubled times there lived a Jewish innkeeper who was forced by the law to serve all kinds of meat, even pork. But, since he was a good Jew, he did not want to cause anyone to eat *treife* food. Yet, how could he tell who was a Jew and who a gentile?

Finally, he found the solution. When a guest came in, he would watch him carefully. If he washed his hands before eating bread, the innkeeper would give him only kosher meat; if he did not, he would receive *treife* meat.

Once, a man entered the inn and asked to be served. The innkeeper put a basket of bread and a pitcher of water on the table, then went to get some food. Out of the corner of his eye he watched to see if the customer washed his hands. When he saw that he did not, he went to the *treife* kitchen and brought back a plate with pork and vegetables. The man ate his meal and then asked for the bill.

"That will be ten coins, please," said the innkeeper.

"Ten coins? But, I don't understand. Just last week I ate here and I only paid eight coins for a meat dinner!"

"I charge ten coins for a pork dinner; it's more than the usual meat dinner," explained the innkeeper.

The man was horrified. "Why did you serve me pork? I am a Jew!"

"How could I have known," the innkeeper said sadly. "Because you did not even wash your hands before the meal, I thought you were a non-Jew! Can you blame me?"

Therefore, our Sages teach us how important it is to wash one's hands before a meal. A person who fails to do so, or forgets, may even come to eat *treife*!

(According to Tanchumah on Parashas Balak 15)

A Pitcher of Water

"וְהִתְקַדִּשְׁתֶּם וִהְיִיתֶם קְדֹשִׁים"

And you shall sanctify yourselves and you shall be holy (11:44)
And you shall be holy — this refers to washing hands
before the meal.

(Tractate Berachos 53b)

The *tana*, R' Akiva, was imprisoned by the Romans for breaking their laws — he had studied and taught the Torah in public. His faithful *talmid*, R' Yehoshua, was allowed to visit him each day to bring him food, for he would not eat anything the warden gave him. And so, each day R' Yehoshua came with a pitcher of water and some bread. He was not allowed to bring anything else.

Once, the guard stopped R' Yehoshua just as he was about to enter the cell. "Show me what you have there!"

R' Yehoshua showed him that all he had was a pitcher of water and some bread. The guard poked the loaf and saw that nothing was concealed inside. Then he looked at the pitcher. It was full to the brim.

"What is your teacher going to do with so much water!" he cried. "He must be planning to escape. He wants to soften the earthen floor so that he can dig his way out." He seized the pitcher and poured out half of the water.

R' Yehoshua came late that day. R' Akiva, who was already old and feeble, asked why he had not come earlier. "I feel weak from hunger," he said. "Give me the water so that I can wash my hands."

R' Yehoshua told his master what had happened. "I only have half the usual amount, *Rebbe*," he said. "How can you use it to wash your hands? You will have nothing left to drink!" Nevertheless, R' Akiva poured the water over his hands and said the blessings over the washing of hands and over bread. After he had eaten the first morsel, he explained, "I have no choice. My colleagues, the *chachamim*, decreed that one must wash hands before eating."

(According to Tractate *Eruvin 21b*)

Shnaps Can Also Help

"וְהִתְקַדִּשְׁתֶּם וִהְיִיתֶם קְדשִׁים"

And you shall sanctify yourselves and you shall be holy (11:44)
And you shall sanctify yourselves — this refers to washing hands before the meal

(Tractate Berachos 53b)

After the death of their leader and shepherd, R'
Elimelech of Lizensk, his chasidim were left bereft.
They mourned the passing of their beloved rebbe, but
knew that they must find a worthy successor. They could
not remain without a guide to show them the way which
they should follow. After much deliberation, they decided
to turn to the saintly brother of their late rebbe, R'
Zusha, who lived in Anipoli. Immediately, two men were
chosen to convey their wishes to R' Zusha.

It was early spring and the ground was soft with the
melting snows. Their famished, boney horses floundered
in the thick, high mud, while their rickety wagon broke
down several times along the way.

During the course of their journey, they reached an inn
close by a hamlet. They were weary and decided to spend
the night there. Upon entering, they discovered that the
innkeeper was a gentile, but he received them warmly
and gave them a clean room for the night.

They were about to go to sleep, exhausted from that
day's traveling, when one of them looked around and
noticed that there was no water in the room.

"How will we wash our hands tomorrow morning?" he
asked. "I'll go to the innkeeper and ask him if he can
spare a basin of water."

With great effort he got up and went to the gentile landlord and asked for some water. The latter apologized, "We finished all the water we had. We have a well but it is quite a distance and the approach to it is too dangerous at night. Tomorrow morning, you will have as much water as you wish." The chasid returned to the room disappointed.

"I am dead tired," said his friend. "Tomorrow I'll think about washing my hands. Anyways, we are really exempt from the *mitzvah*." And he fell asleep as soon as his head touched the pillow.

But his companion did not sleep. True, they were not required to fulfill the *mitzvah*, but his heart would not be still. His eyelids drooped, his head dropped and still he drove sleep away.

Finally, he had an idea. He left his room quickly and sought out the innkeeper. It was already late and he was sleeping. However, the chasid woke him up and said that he wished to buy a bottle of shnaps.

"What do you mean, waking me up at such an inconvenient hour?" said the landlord angrily. "I had already fallen asleep. Well, if you really want me to get up for you, you will have to pay double!"

The chasid agreed and got his bottle of shnaps. He put it by his bedside and with a sigh of relief, dropped off to sleep.

The next morning, he washed his hands with the liquor and said his prayers. His friend decided to delay washing his hands until they reached a source of water. They were already delayed and had to be on their way.

That very afternoon, they arrived at their journey's end, Anipoli.

They went directly to R' Zusha's humble home,

knocked on the door and were told to enter.

"Shalom, Rebbe!" they said. R' Zusha looked at them, then concentrated his gaze upon the chasid who had not washed his hands in the morning. "Do you know," he said to him, "that all of the impurity and grime which my holy brother succeeded in cleansing away throughout all of his years in Lizensk has returned overnight, just because you did not wash your hands this morning?"

The guilty chasid burst into tears and his friend trembled. Truly, this was a man worthy of replacing their departed rebbe.

He Saves Man and Beast

"וְהִתְקַדִּשְׁתֶּם וִהְיִיתֶם קְדשִׁים"

And you shall sanctify yourselves and you shall be holy (11:44)
And you should be holy — this refers to washing hands
before the meal

(Tractate Berachos 53b)

A simple wagoner once came to R' Yisrael Yitzchak of Alexander with a strange problem.

"My horse refuses to eat! I put hay and oats before him yet he refuses to touch them. If this continues, he will soon die and I will have no source of livelihood!" he said.

"Tell me some more," the Rebbe said. "Tell me about your own eating habits."

"Well," the wagoner began matter-of-factly. "I wash my hands for breakfast right after my morning prayers. I grab a sandwich, which I usually eat on the road, and have a snack whenever I find the time during the day. Then, at night, before going to bed, I say the *birchas hamazon.*"

"Aha!" said the Rebbe, "there's your reason. Because you eat like an animal, your horse wished to eat like a human being. If you decide to eat like a man ought to, your horse will eat his hay — like an animal."

Impure and Pure

"זֹאת תּוֹרַת הַבְּהֵמָה וְהָעוֹף... לְהַבְדִּיל בֵּין הַטָּמֵא וּבֵין הַטָּהֹר"

These are the laws of the animal and the fowl... to differentiate between the impure and between the pure (11:46-47)

"**M**y mother asked me to show this chicken stomach to you," the little boy said, holding it out to R' Avraham Chaim of Zlotchov for examination. "She wants to know if the chicken is kosher or not."

It was a chicken stomach, like any other. R' Avraham Chaim took it, turned it all around and inside out. There seemed to be nothing wrong with it at all. Still, something told him to reject it, to rule this chicken *treife.*

R' Chaim of Tchernowitz, who happened to be present at the time, looked at it, also. He examined it very carefully. He could not understand what was troubling R' Avraham Chaim, why he was hesitating, what was preventing him from ruling it kosher and sending the boy back home.

Imagine his surprise when R' Avraham Chaim pronounced it *treife*! He could not help bursting out, "Pardon me, but, according to the *Shulchan Aruch*, there is no reason why the chicken should not be kosher! What in the world made you rule otherwise?"

"What can I do?" R' Avraham Chaim said apologetically. "I can see nothing wrong with it either. But my heart tells me that the chicken is *treife*. I cannot go against my instinct. Perhaps this chicken is forbidden due to some other flaw."

"Did you bring the rest of the chicken with you?" R' Chaim asked the boy. He shook his head. "Well then, be a good boy. Run home and fetch it."

Before long he returned with the entire bird. R' Avraham Chaim examined it and said, "Aha! See! The foot is broken. This makes the bird absolutely *treife*. You see, I was right after all!"

R' Chaim looked at him with awe, then said, "Now I understand the prayer in which we ask that we not be responsible for any stumbling block or mishap, that we not err in any *halachic* matter and that we not pronounce something impure as pure."

All Because of the Shochtim

"לְהַבְדִּיל בֵּין הַטָּמֵא וּבֵין הַטָּהֹר"

To differentiate between what is impure and between what is
pure (11:47)

"... (to differentiate) what is impure to you from what is
pure to you: whether half of the windpipe has been
slaughtered or the greater part of it.

(Rashi)

The *Ohev Yisrael* of Apta once related the following story to his chasidim to show them the importance of having G-d-fearing *shochtim* in one's city:

A terrible epidemic had broken out in Yaroslav, attacking the young children. It spread from house to house and the people were helpless to stop it. Desperate, the community decided to send a delegation to the great *tzaddik* who lived not far away, the famous R' Elimelech of Lizensk, to seek his advice and beg him to pray for their children.

R' Elimelech turned to those who were sent and said, "Am I a prophet, or the son of a prophet, to know why the children are dying?" But, seeing that you have come to me I tell you that it would be wise of you to keep a close eye on the *shochtim* in your city."

The delegation returned to Yaroslav and, immediately, the community appointed a G-d-fearing overseer, a scholar of integrity and experience, to supervise the affairs of the slaughterhouse.

One day the inspector happened to overhear a conversation. One of the older *shochtim* said to a newcomer in a whisper, "Hey, watch what you are doing.

You can't do that here any more. We are being watched by the new inspector."

These few words were enough to show him that R' Elimelech, in his divine intuition, had seen the cause of the epidemic.

The new supervisor reported the conversation to the rabbi of the city and the entire staff of *shochtim* was dismissed. They were replaced by sincere, practiced *shochtim* who feared *Hashem*.

At once, the epidemic halted and the children began to recover.

Genuine Respect for the Torah

"וְדָוִד מְכַרְכֵּר בְּכָל עֹז לִפְנֵי ה'"

And David danced before Hashem with all his might
(Haftorah Parashas Shemini, Shmuel II 6:14)

The small community of Tveryah in *Eretz Yisrael* had put on a festive air. You could feel it everywhere. Everyone was in their *yom tov* best, eagerly awaiting the special joyous occasion, the completion and dedication of a new *sefer Torah* for their small synagogue.

The Jewish community did not number many families, but, just a few years earlier, there had been no Jewish settlement at all in this city of Galilee! However, in the year 5500 (1740), R' Chaim Abulafya had come to settle here along with his family and disciples. The new settlers worked hard to restore the ruins of a destroyed city.

Before long, they had built a synagogue and *mikveh*, thanks to the energy of the tireless R' Chaim, who, even at the age of eighty, urged his followers on. Within a few years, Tveryah was a community that he could be proud of!

Settling in *Eretz Yisrael* and rebuilding its ruins had always been a dream close to R' Chaim Abulafya's heart. Born in Chevron, he had taken it upon himself, as a young man, to travel throughout the Diaspora collecting funds to help sustain the Jewish communities in the Holy Land; the land was barren and eking out a living was close to impossible. His travels led R' Chaim, finally, to Izmir, Turkey, where he was asked to remain and serve as rabbi.

His love for *Eretz Yisrael* never waned, however. From here, he was able to send huge sums to support the Jewish settlements. Finally, towards the end of his life, he returned with his family and followers to restore the city of Tveryah and reestablish a Jewish community there.

The writing of a new *sefer Torah* and its dedication, the *hachnasas sefer Torah*, was a great milestone for the city. Everyone shared the excitement and joy; everyone was united in a feeling of holiness and accomplishment. So much so, that the townspeople gathered in front of their venerable rabbi's home hours before the scheduled event.

"Our rabbi must be preparing himself for this holy event too. He must be concentrating upon all kinds of holy mystical Names and thoughts," they whispered to one another and kept a respectful silence, patiently awaiting for the appointed hour to arrive.

It, finally, did. The elder members of the community walked up to the door of the rabbi's house and knocked gently. There was no response. They knocked again, somewhat harder. Someone answered the door, saying that the rabbi had left a long time before. While they were still puzzling over the message, some little boys came running, puffing and panting, with the news that the rabbi was already at the *beis knesses*.

"And do you know what we saw!" one little boy said. "The rabbi had a broom. He was sweeping the courtyard!"

Shocked and dazed, the entire group rushed to the *beis knesses*.

Sure enough! There was the eighty-year-old rabbi, broom in hand, sweeping the square in front of the synagogue.

"What are you doing, Rebbe?!" they spluttered. "Is this *kavod haTorah*?! Is this how you show respect for the Torah, by sweeping the courtyard yourself? You are the rabbi!"

"And what, pray tell, is wrong with sweeping a synagogue courtyard?" the old man replied humbly. "This, too, is considered respect for the Torah. Today, we will all be gathering here to celebrate. This morning, I noticed that the courtyard was all dusty and littered. I knew that no one would think to clean it up; everyone would have other matters on their mind. So, I decided I would do it myself. Yes, this, too, is *kavod haTorah*!"

The people of Tveryah bowed their heads. The rabbi was right. And the prominent members of the *kehillah* said, "Where you see his humility — therein lies his greatness! King David 'lowered' himself to honor the Torah by dancing in the streets and yet, this humble act was actually a sign of his greatness. So, R' Chaim Abulafya 'humbled' himself by sweeping the courtyard in honor of the *hachnasas sefer Torah*."

The Dancing 'Grandfather'

"מְפַזֵּז וּמְכַרְכֵּר לִפְנֵי ה'"

Dancing before Hashem
(Haftorah Parashas Shemini, Shmuel II 6:16)

The people of Shpoli always awaited the *Shabbos*
eagerly. For Friday night in Shpoli was something
special. On Friday night the Shpoli Zeide, as the Rebbe
was affectionately called by his chasidim, would dance.
And everyone felt the holiness which burst forth from
the dance.

One who never saw the Zeide dance, cannot begin to
imagine what an impact his 'performance' had upon
people. The Rebbe would begin humming a tune then lift
a hand here, a finger there and poise his foot with a
spiritual grace that created an atmosphere of *kedushah*,
such as one did not even feel on *Yom Kippur*. People
would stand entranced, for hours at a time, watching the
Rebbe speak with his hands, pray with his body, express
holy thoughts through every movement, nuance and
gesture. It was an indescribable experience. And if you
had once seen the Shpoli Zeide dance, you were never
the same. The Zeide's dance opened up a new dimension
in people's hearts, a new scope in G-dly worship, like the
lifting of a veil into a new, spiritual world. To look at the
Zeide while he was dancing was to see a person
transported beyond his physical casing, soaring to other
spheres, other worlds. Who guided those graceful hands?
Who directed the orchestration of other-worldly beauty
that was expressed through his every movement?

People in Shpoli looked forward to Friday evenings for an experience that took them away from their everyday cares and gave them a true taste of *olam haba*. This was sanctity; this was *kedushah*.

R' Avraham the *Malach* (Angel), son of the celebrated Maggid of Mezeritch, also, felt that ecstasy of holiness. Marveling at the sheer holiness of the Zeide's movements, he watched him carefully, observing every single step with his discerning eye.

Later, when the Zeide had finished and was seated at the *Shabbos* table with his guest, the latter exclaimed, "Now I know what it means to 'dance before the bride, Queen *Shabbos*'! While you dance I could distinguish a holy thought behind every single motion, every lift of your eyebrow!"

The Shpoli Zeide said, "I am able to dance thus, thanks to a blessing I once received from the holy Baal Shem Tov."

"But you keep such perfect time to the music! Someone must have taught you the art of dancing!"

The Shpoli Zeide nodded. "You are right. I was taught how to dance. You smile? But it is absolutely true! I had dancing lessons from an expert teacher — from Eliyahu Hanavi himself! I see that you are curious. Well then, settle back to listen, for it is a long story":

Before I settled in Shpoli, I used to wander from place to place, befriending unfortunate Jews and trying to do some good, wherever I could. At one village, I learned about a poor Jewish tenant who, unable to pay his rent, had been thrown into a dungeon by his anti-Semitic overseer.

It was a very common practice of the times. The debtors' prisons were full of tenants who had not met payments. Instead of allowing them to work off their debts, their hard-hearted overseers or landowners threw them into prison. Sometimes, a man's family or acquaintances would collect money to pay off his debts and redeem him. Sometimes, the poor man languished in jail until he died.

But, often the poor Jewish tenant remained in his dungeon receiving meager rations until the birthday of the landowner. On that day the landowner held a grand banquet for his friends and, when all were pleasantly satisfied with food and drink, he had the Jew brought up and dressed in a bearskin.

And then, he was ordered to dance to the music. But not just dance. There were special rules to this 'game'. The bear would be led on a chain by the overseer. The two would then have a dancing competition. If the overseer danced more agilely and gracefully than the bear, he would have the pleasure of taking the bear out to the courtyard where starving hounds would rip him to pieces. If — and no one dreamed of this possibility — the bear was the superior dancer, he would be allowed to pounce upon his overseer, beat him to his heart's content and gain his freedom.

Imagine a poor Jew thrown into a dungeon. For months, he had not seen the light of day. All he had for food was the bread and water, which were lowered down into his pit once a week. He was so weakened that he could barely put one foot ahead of the other, let alone dance. This, then was the fate which awaited our prisoner.

One day, after I had heard the story, Eliyahu Hanavi came to me and unfolded a marvelous plan. I was to dress up in the bearskin, take the place of the unfortunate prisoner and dance so well that I would be judged to have won the contest.

But who would teach me to dance, I asked fearfully. Eliyahu Hanavi promised to teach me himself. He would tell me exactly what to do. I need only follow instructions. That is when I received my dancing lessons.

The day of the party arrived. It was early evening when I reached the edge of the dungeon pit. I took advantage of the general excitement and the fact that the usual guards were already drunk on the nobleman's wine. The music was blaring and the guests had already begun to arrive.

The prisoner was alarmed by my appearance, but I calmed him. Standing above him at the edge of pit, I called down, "Psssst. Listen here. I have come to rescue you. I am going to exchange places with you. I will put on your clothing and, when they come to take me, I will wear the bearskin and will dance for the *poritz*."

"But you will never outdance the overseer. He is a healthy peasant, an expert in the Russian Cossack dances. You will be exhausted before he has even warmed up!" the prisoner warned me.

"Don't you worry about me! Just hold onto this rope and let me pull you out."

He grasped hold of the end of the rope and held on. But when I pulled on it, he fell back, too weak to even let me pull him up.

"Wait," I said. "Here is some food and shnaps. These should strengthen you. Eat and drink and then we will try again."

A short while later, he stood next to me, stretching his cramped limbs.

We exchanged clothes and I saw him on his way. Then

I lowered myself into the pit.

I did not have much time for thinking. Soon I could hear footsteps approaching. They were not too steady. "Fine," I thought, "if he is already drunk, my work will be that much easier!"

A key grated in the lock and the cell door rattled. The iron door creaked open and a coarse voice urged me to get up. I staggered to my feet, pretending to be weaker than I was, lest the overseer suspect anything. He yanked me out and quickly thrust me into a stifling bearskin. The prisoner would surely have fallen under its very weight, I thought.

I was pulled roughly along, half walking half dragged. I could hear the music getting louder. A few more steps and we were inside a huge ballroom. A band played up our entrance which was greeted by thunderous applause.

Shouts of excitement greeted us from all sides.

"They are here."

"Now the fun will begin."

"This will be excellent sport."

But the host, the nobleman, demanded silence. "There are rules to this sport, you know," he said to his audience. A man dressed up as a hangman, all in black, entered, a long scroll held in his right hand. He unfurled it and began reading in a loud monotone, "The Jew and the overseer will now enter a dancing contest. If the Jew can keep in time to the music without faltering, he will gain his freedom. If he shows that he is an even better dancer than his 'leader', he will be allowed to beat him."

Shouts of laughter accompanied this statement. No one expected the bear to last for even the first dance! The hangman silenced them with one dark stare from under his thick, bushy eyebrows. Then he continued, "But if the 'leader' outdances his partner, the bear, then he will be allowed to throw the bear to the bloodhounds who have not been fed for several days." He rolled up the scroll, clicked his heels and marched out of the hall.

The nobleman now gave the sign for the music to begin. The overseer yanked at the iron chain, pulling me to my feet. The band was playing a waltz. I lifted my feet and began dancing in time to the music, slowly whirling around, gracefully, even in my unwieldy bear costume. The audience stared at me, dumbfounded. No one expected a Jew to know how to dance, least of all, one who had just come out of prison and was encumbered with a bulky, hot bear costume. Even the overseer had stopped dancing to watch me, but was reprimanded by the nobleman.

"You must dance alongside the bear if you do not want to forfeit the contest," he said. His guests clapped their hands in agreement. This was excellent entertainment, a bear-Jew who actually knew how to dance!

The music came to an end, but, before we two dancers could catch our breath, it had struck up a lively tune, a Cossatchke. The overseer, a former Russian soldier, was expert at this. He kicked out his feet, right and left, beads of sweat streaming down his face, his arms outstretched to maintain balance. He heard a deafening applause and looked up to smile at his audience when, suddenly, he realized that they were not applauding him. They were cheering for me, the bear, who with all of my weight and bulk, was also squatting and kicking out my heels, faster and faster, in time to the music. The overseer tried to keep up, but felt his age. He had also gained weight since his army days and his muscles had become flaccid. After five minutes of exertion he fell flat

on his face. I was still going strong, gathering momentum as I went along.

The music stopped and the overseer got to his feet, panting and mopping his brow. He grabbed a drink from one of the tables and then gave a sign to the musicians to strike up the band again, motioning to them to change the tempo.

The band played and the two figures danced. The more tired the overseer grew, the more energetic the bear seemed to get. "There must be a devil inside that costume," I heard the anti-Semite muttering, gnashing his teeth but not giving up the fight. The crowd was enjoying this tremendously. While at first, they had cheered their companion, the gentile overseer, they soon began changing sides and were now urging the bear on. They had never seen such grace, such perfect timing, such intricate dance steps. They were entranced. The band played on, sometimes slow, sometimes fast — the drums booming, horns blasting, violinists bowing furiously. Faster and faster, louder and louder.

At last, the overseer collapsed, moaning. He could not summon up the strength to move. There was no doubt that I, the Jew, was the winner of the contest. I now pounced upon the overseer, beating him furiously, striking blows right and left, with a vengeance, for all the ill treatment which the real tenant had suffered over the years.

The crowd was stunned. Nothing like this had ever happened. It was always the Jew who had fallen down. But, suddenly, the comedy of the scene struck them, and the justice of it. The Jew had outwitted the overseer. How, they did not know. But fair was fair. He had won this contest and was claiming his just reward.

I was getting carried away with myself. I felt the burden of my entire people. I struck out as if to avenge the blood of all my brethren. After a few minutes, however, the nobleman came to me and laid a resisting hand upon my arm. "That is enough. You may return home. You are free again. Your debt is canceled. Tomorrow we begin a fresh account."

Still wearing my bear costume, I left the hall and made for the tenant's home. He was surprised, but overjoyed to see me alive and whole. I told him exactly what had happened and he rejoiced to hear that I had taken revenge, for all the beatings he had suffered from the overseer.

The story was over and the Shpoli Zeide turned to his guest, R' Avraham the *Malach*, and said, "And now you see where I learned to dance. I had such an excellent teacher that I have never forgotten that art."

R' Avraham sighed wistfully, "Yes. And your dances express far more than I might hope to with my most fervent prayers."

The Chafetz Chaim Makes a Bed

"וּנְקַלֹּתִי עוֹד מִזֹּאת וְהָיִיתִי שָׁפָל בְּעֵינָי"

And I will yet be more vile than this and would be lowly in my own sight
(Haftorah Parashas Shemini, Shmuel II 6:22)

The Chafetz Chaim's home was like a magnet, drawing people from all over the world. And yet everyone who came was treated warmly and personally, by none other than the host himself.

The Chafetz Chaim set the table, served the food, made up the beds and made sure that his guests lacked nothing.

The Chafetz Chaim lived to a ripe old age. But, even when he was in his seventies and eighties, he insisted on attending to his guests personally.

Once, a visitor accepted the Chafetz Chaim's invitation to stay overnight. Not knowing of his custom of serving guests himself, the visitor was astonished to see the old man bustling around the house, fetching a pillow from here, fresh linen from there. His amazement reached a climax when he saw the old sage struggling with the wide sheets and the featherbed. He rushed forward to help him, embarrassed to be served like this and to be causing the Chafetz Chaim so much bother.

"Please," he begged. "Let me make up the bed myself. It is too much of a strain for you!"

The Chafetz Chaim ignored him and the guest was too embarrassed to insist. Perhaps, the old man had not heard him.

The next morning they went to *shul* together. Just as the visitor was about to put on his *tefillin*, the Chafetz Chaim walked up to him and said, "Wait, perhaps I can help you with that?"

The visitor looked at the old sage, utterly bewildered. Help in putting on one's *tefillin*?! "B-b-b-but that is a *mitzvah* which a person is required to do himself!

The Chafetz Chaim's eyes twinkled with good humor. "Do you hear what you are saying?! There is no difference between the *mitzvah* of *tefillin* and that of *hachnasas orchim*, hospitality. Just as you refuse to let anyone else put your *tefillin* on for you, so do I refuse to let anyone perform the *mitzvah* of attending to my guests for me! I have to perform that *mitzvah* — not my guest."

R'Zusha Learns a Lesson

"וְהָיִיתִי שָׁפָל בְּעֵינַי"
And I would be lowly in my own sight
(Haftorah Parashas Shemini, Shmuel II, 6:22)

R' Zusha of Anipoli was poverty-stricken all of his life. Once, however, he acquired a ten ruble note which, for him, was a huge sum, something to put away. He opened a *chumash Vayikra* to the *parashah* of *Kedoshim* and inserted it at the page where 'You shall not steal' appeared.

Somehow, this became known to a thief. He crept into the house, removed the ten ruble bill and replaced it with a five ruble note, inserting this just a few pages further, by the verse where it is stated, 'Love your neighbor as yourself.'

A few days later R' Zusha needed the money. He opened the *chumash* to the page where he had placed the ten ruble note. It was gone. "That's strange," he thought, as he leafed through the pages to see if it had been misplaced. There, just a few pages further, he found the five ruble note. R' Zusha looked at the page and understood. There were the words, 'Love your neighbor as yourself.' He was deeply moved.

Lifting up the five ruble note, he exclaimed, "How holy are Your people, *Hashem*! And how base and lowly is Zusha! Zusha had ten whole rubles and took them all for himself! Along comes another Jew, a thief no less, who refused to take the entire sum for himself. He took five for himself and left five for Zusha, thus fulfilling the commandment of 'Love your neighbor.' Ah! How precious are the Jewish people!"

פָּרָשַׁת תַּזְרִיעַ

Parashas Tazriya

A Good Meal

"וּבַיּוֹם הַשְּׁמִינִי יִמּוֹל... עָרְלָתוֹ"

And on the eighth day he shall be circumcised (12:3)

No celebration took place in Berditchov, be it a wedding, a *bar mitzvah* or a *bris* without the beloved rabbi, R' Levi Yitzchak, being invited to participate.

Whenever he was invited to a *bris* he had a standard answer, "I will be glad to come, but on one condition."

"And what is that, Rebbe?" the man would ask.

"I will come only, if you give a decent meal afterwards."

People knew what the Rebbe was going to say and wondered. The Rebbe certainly did not come for the meal. What a ridiculous thought. The Rebbe was not concerned about food.

Finally, one of the townspeople could not contain his curiosity. When it came his turn to invite the Rebbe to a *bris*, he burst out, "Rebbe, tell me, why are you so interested in the meal?"

"Let me explain. I have a constant battle with the Satan. I defend the Jewish people before the Heavenly

Throne and seek to put them in a favorable light, while he prosecutes, always finding fault with them, so that they will be punished. I come before the Heavenly court and admit that it happens, occasionally, that a Jew sins. But does anyone ever rejoice over his sin? Does anyone ever celebrate having erred? Of course not. On the other hand, when a Jew performs a *mitzvah* — a *bris* or a *bar mitzvah*, then he is joyous, then he does hold a feast and rejoices.

"Is this not the perfect argument against the Satan? Well, the Satan knows this and, therefore, always tries to prevent the Jew from celebrating at those occasions of *mitzvos*. That is why I insist on coming only, if I know, in advance, that each *mitzvah* will be accompanied by a decent celebration... to seal the Satan's lips."

The Prophet Did Not Err

"יָבֹא נָא אֵלַי וְיֵדַע כִּי יֵשׁ נָבִיא בְּיִשְׂרָאֵל"

Let him come to me and he will know that there is a prophet in Israel
(Haftorah Parashas Tazriya, Melachim II 5:8)

In the period of the Crusades, Godfried, a Christian duke, was about to set out at the head of his troops to conquer Jerusalem, the Holy City, from the Moslems.

He had heard of the famous Jewish sage, R' Shlomo Yitzchak, Rashi, who was said to be exceptionally wise and could even foretell the future. Godfried wished to meet with him before setting out on his dangerous campaign.

The duke arrived and told Rashi, "I have amassed a huge army of trained men and mighty horses. I am going forth to capture Jerusalem and free it from Moslem rule. I have no doubt that victory will be mine. Still, I wished to consult with you, to hear what you have to say. I wish to hear your prediction, even if it is unfavorable. Do not be afraid. Be forthright. I know that you are a holy man and whatever you say will come true."

"Your Excellency, the Duke," replied Rashi, "you will not be happy to hear my forecast. You will be victorious and you will succeed in capturing Jerusalem, but your victory will be short-lived. You will rule for only three days. Your entire army will be wiped out in a bloody battle and you will return home with only three horses."

Godfried was shocked and crushed. In his anger and frustration, he lashed out at the Jewish sage, pointed an accusing finger and said, "You may be right. But, if I return from my Crusade with four horses instead of three, I will have you thrown to the dogs and all the Jews in my kingdom will be destroyed!" And with these parting words Godfried stamped out of the room, much less confidently than he had come.

When all of his preparations were completed, Godfried took his immense army, marched through France and on to the Middle East. Everything happened just as Rashi had predicted. In a stormy battle he succeeded in routing the Moslems from Jerusalem.

Three days later, the Arabs retaliated, wiping out his forces in a bloody massacre. And so, crushed and defeated, he turned homewards. The way home took four lengthy years and he finally arrived astride a horse and three more mounted soldiers straggling behind. All the while, he seethed with anger.

"The Jewish sage promised that I would return with three horses and I have come back with four! I will punish him," thought Godfried throughout his long journey. "As soon as I enter the city, I will fulfill my threat. I will cast him to the dogs."

Hashem in heaven was not quite finished with Godfried, however. For just as he was passing through the city gates, a huge stone became dislodged and tumbled down, crushing the last horse and rider of the tiny caravan.

Godfried had barely missed being crushed to death himself and sighed with relief, but he realized that Rashi's prediction had come true, after all. He felt very humbled. He dismounted and hat in hand, walked all the way to Rashi's *beis midrash* to tell the Jewish sage how sorry he was to have doubted him and to pay his respects.

But, when he arrived, he found a huge crowd in front of the building. People were weeping and sobbing.

"What is the matter?" he inquired.

"Our sage, Rashi, has just died," people informed him. Godfried stepped inside the house and saw the chair empty. Instead there was a large coffin in the room. The funeral was about to leave for the Jewish cemetery.

Many, many people attended the funeral of the great sage, Rashi, and among the mourners was a man who had known Rashi for only a few moments. This gentile accompanied the coffin along with the rest. He, too, mourned the passing of a great man.

The Tzaddik's Holy Vision

"יָבֹא נָא אֵלַי וְיֵדַע כִּי יֵשׁ נָבִיא בְּיִשְׂרָאֵל"

Let him come to me and he will know that there is a prophet in
Israel
(Haftorah Parashas Tazriya, Melachem II 5:8)

E ven in his old age, R' Leib Sarah's (he was called this
after his righteous mother) still traveled from place
to place, helping out his brethren. But he did not travel
alone. He was accompanied by R' Azriel of Polochak, a
talmid of the Maggid of Mezeritch.

Once, as they were nearing Vilna, they stopped at the
inn of a wealthy Jew and took a room for the night.

The next morning, before they were about to leave, R'
Leib asked R' Azriel to summon the innkeeper to his
room. When he stood before him, R' Leib said, "I want
you to go to the section of the city where the aristocracy
live. Go to the prince's palace and demand that he come
to me at once. Tell him that R' Leib Sarah's wants to see
him."

The innkeeper looked at his guest as if he were mad.
"What do you take me for, an utter fool? A madman?
Don't you know that any Jew that steps foot on that
street is as good as dead! And that prince, the king's son,
has never had any dealings whatsoever with Jews. How
can I dare walk into the lion's den and tell the prince that
a Jew summons him?"

R' Leib spoke harshly to the innkeeper, "I see that my
name does not mean anything to you. Well, let me tell
you, if you do not do as I say, you will regret it."

The words had hardly left his mouth when a cry was heard. The innkeeper's wife and children had, suddenly, been attacked by illness. The innkeeper ran to their side. They were in great pain and seemed about to die. With faltering steps he returned and begged his guest to help him.

"Your only hope is to do as I ordered. You must go to the prince at once," said R' Leib, "before it is too late, and give him my message. Tell him that Leib Sarah's wishes to see him at once. If you do so, your family will be healed."

Trembling like a windblown leaf, the innkeeper started walking. He reached the exclusive neighborhood. To his surprise, nothing happened and he quickly reached the prince's palace.

He lifted the big brass knocker and let it fall. The doorman answered the knock. He did not even seem surprised to see a Jew upon the threshold. "What do you want?" he asked.

"I want to see the prince. I have a message for him."

The butler turned on his heel, returning in a moment. "The prince says that you are to be shown in."

The Jew was quickly ushered into a large drawing room. Here the prince sat, upon a luxurious armchair, not surprised at his visitor. The innkeeper delivered his message, his knees knocking and voice trembling. To his amazement, as soon as the prince heard him mention the name 'Leib Sarah's', his face turned pale. He nodded.

"I will come with you at once," the prince said. He donned a cloak and, shortly afterwards, they left the palace and went directly to the inn where R' Leib awaited them.

R' Leib dismissed the innkeeper, telling him to see how

his family was faring. Meanwhile, he led the prince inside the room and shut the door. The two remained there for some time. Then the door opened, the prince left and R' Leib told R' Azriel to prepare their wagon, for they would now continue their journey.

The prince could not understand his own actions. What had prompted him to follow the Jewish innkeeper? What spell had that name, Leib Sarah's, cast over him? He was thoroughly confused, for he had never heard that name before! What strange magnet had drawn him to the Jewish inn? As soon as he was back in his palace, he ordered his servants to go to the inn and fetch the elderly Jew, R' Leib, to him at once.

The servants returned emptyhanded. The Jew had already left.

Time passed and the strange incident was forgotten. It was just before *Pesach* when misfortune befell the wealthy Jewish innkeeper. His gentile servant had disappeared. Gentiles seized upon this and accused him of murdering his servant and using the blood to bake *matzos*. The authorities believed them and threw the innocent Jew into jail. No questions were asked.

The police tortured him, trying to extract a confession. At first he resisted firmly, holding out under the pain and suffering. He refused to confess to a crime he had not committed. But with time, he grew weaker; he longed for the suffering to cease. There came a time when he felt that death would be a sweet release from the terrible tortures. And so he finally gave in, signing the confession which the police had drawn up.

The court held a quick trial. Since he had already confessed, the judge sentenced the 'guilty' Jew to death. But before the punishment could be carried out, the

prince of the region had to sign the death warrant.
Surprisingly, though, the prince begged for a delay.

"In a few days," he said, "there is going to be horse fair
in the city. I have heard that this innkeeper is an expert
on horses. I want to take him along with me to the fair
to buy some horses. After that I will sign the death
warrant and you can carry out the death sentence."

The authorities had no choice but to wait until after
the fair.

A few days later the prince took the Jewish prisoner
and traveled to the fair to buy some horses. The Jew did
not forget, for a moment, that he was a prisoner
sentenced to death, for he had two armed guards by his
side all the while.

The fair itself lasted for several days. On one of those
days, as the Jew was inspecting a group of horses, he,
suddenly, saw a familiar figure. He rubbed his eyes, not
believing what they told him. He ran up to the man.
There was his gentile servant, the one whom he had
been accused of murdering! Master and servant fell upon
one another's necks, weeping with joy.

"Oh master!" said the servant. "How glad I am to see
you! How I longed to return to you. I have had a terrible
time. You probably wondered what had happened to me
and assumed that I had run away. But I would never run
away from you; you treated me like a father does a son.
You fed me well, clothed me and paid me decently... But
a priest persuaded me to come with him and promised
that he would give me a plot of land of my own and a
house. I did not even consider his offer, knowing that I
was best off with you. And so he came one night with
some other men, tied me up, threw me into a wagon and
carried me far away. No house and field were awaiting

me there, like they promised. No such thing! They threw me out and drove off quickly. After much effort I succeeded in freeing myself. I was in a strange city. Since then I have been wandering the roads, begging my bread. How I longed to return to you but the road back was long and I had not a penny with which to travel."

"What brought you here to the horse fair?" his master asked.

"It is strange that you ask. I had no intentions of coming here. But last night, an elderly Jew stopped me on the road and asked me if I wanted a lift. I climbed into his wagon and sat there, next to his attendant. I was so tired that I fell asleep, not caring where I was going. When morning dawned the old man woke me up and said, 'Here we are, at the horse fair. You will find your master here.' And so, here, I am. I have been wandering around all day, looking for you. How glad I am to have found you! Please take me back with you, if you do not, I will die of starvation!"

The innkeeper realized, immediately, that the elderly Jew had been none other than his amazing guest, R' Leib Sarah's.

He took his servant to a restaurant and let him eat his fill, bidding him to remain there until he came to fetch him. Meanwhile, he returned to the prince who was waiting for him.

"My business is all finished," said the prince. "I have selected excellent horses, thanks to you. But now we must return."

The two men entered the coach. Suddenly, the horses reared. They were unmanageable. The Jewish innkeeper turned to the prince and said, "At the fair I met a man who has an excellent hand with horses. I believe that he could control these wayward horses. Shall I fetch him?"

The prince agreed. The Jew ran back to the fair and quickly returned in the company of his servant. The servant climbed up on the driver's seat and took hold of the reins. Immediately, the high-spirited animals became docile and they were soon under way.

While still on the road, the prince turned to the Jew and said, "Do you recall the visit you paid me several months ago, bidding me come to your inn because an old Jew wished to see me?"

"Oh yes, I remember that well!" the innkeeper nodded.

"Did you never wonder what he said to me when we were alone in the room?"

"Of course I did," said the Jew.

"He asked me for just one favor. He said that the time would come when you would be imprisoned and I would be asked to sign your death warrant. When that time came, he said, I was to request a delay until after we went to the annual horse fair. That was all. Can you understand that request? It was strange to me at the time and is still a riddle. I don't know why I agreed. Perhaps, because I saw that he was a saintly person. And when his prediction came true, I had no choice but to keep my promise. I thought that this trip would help you somehow, but here we are, returning from the fair and nothing has changed. When we arrive, I will have to turn you over to the authorities. Of what purpose then was this trip. Can you explain this to me?"

The Jew was calm, far less excited than the puzzled prince. "When we get back," he said, "I will have my defense all ready. Do you know, Your Highness, who the new wagoner is? He is the missing servant whom I am accused of having murdered! He was kidnapped by a priest and taken far, far away. They thought that, if he ever returned, I would already be dead. If you don't believe me, you can ask my servant yourself."

The prince was astounded at the turn of events, all the more so, when he learned who had brought the servant to the fair.

"That elderly Jew was truly a godly person, a prophet," he said. "I see that there is a G-d in Israel Who protects His people.

"But why did you confess to the murder if you were innocent? You hurt not only yourself but your people." The Jew burst out tearfully, "I was tortured in prison. I was beaten, starved, cursed. It became so unbearable that I preferred to die rather than to continue suffering. It just goes to show how valid are these 'confessions' extracted from us by the police."

The rest of the trip passed in pleasant conversation and, before they knew it, they had reached their destination.

The prince drove straight to the authorities and demanded that a special court session be convened to review the case. Then he produced the new evidence, the 'murdered' servant. He related all that had happened and the judges had no choice but to free the Jew with their apologies.

Alexander the Great and Shimon Hatzaddik

"יָדַעְתִּי כִּי אֵין אֱ־לֹהִים בְּכָל הָאָרֶץ כִּי אִם בְּיִשְׂרָאֵל"

*I know that G-d is not to be found in all the land except in
Yisrael
(Haftorah Parashas Tazriya, Melachim II 5:15)*

The Kusim hated the Jews and constantly plotted against them. They would slander them before the rulers of *Eretz Yisrael*.

When Alexander the Great was master over most of the world, the Kusim came to him saying that the Jews planned to rebel against him. He believed them and gave them permission to destroy the *Beis Hamikdash* and to do as they pleased to the Jews.

When the Jews learned of this, in their despair, they turned to their leader, the *gadol hador*, Shimon Hatzaddik, hoping that he could thwart the Kusim.

Shimon Hatzaddik, the *Kohen Gadol*, put on his priestly garments and selected a delegation of the nation's most distinguished sages. They set out, in procession, at nightfall, torches lighting their way. Towards morning they reached Alexander's camp.

Alexander saw them coming from afar and asked the local inhabitants, the Kusim, who was approaching.

"Those are the rebellious Jews," he was told.

When they stood before the king, Alexander the Great descended from his royal chariot and prostrated himself at Shimon Hatzaddik's feet.

The Kusim, witnessing the king's strange behavior, said in amazement, "Why is Your Majesty, a great and mighty king, bowing before a Jew?!"

The king turned to them and replied, "The image of this elderly man appears before me in a dream preceding each battle I wage and tells me that I will be victorious. How shall I not bow down before him?" He then turned to the Jewish delegation and said, "And why have you come to me?"

They replied, "You have wicked enemies, the Kusim, who despise us and wish to cause strife in this land by slandering us. They lied when they told you that we wish to rebel. That is the furthest thought from our minds. We are a peace-loving people. It is the Kusim who are quarrel-mongers. They sought to destroy our *Beis Hamikdash*, the holy place where we pray for your success and welfare. And Your Majesty granted them permission to do so."

Alexander then said in anger, "I deliver the Kusim into your hands. Do to them as you see fit."

The Jews seized them, bound them to horses and dragged them all the way to Mount Grizim, where they had settled. The Jews then destroyed the temple of the Kusim on Mount Grizim, razing it to the ground, doing to them as they had intended doing to the Jews.

And that day was established in Jewish history as a day of celebration, a *yom tov*, commemorating the miracle that had happened.

(Yalkut Shimoni Shemos 1101)

פָּרָשַׁת מְצֹרָע

Parashas Metzora

The Marvelous Medicine

"זֹאת תִּהְיֶה תּוֹרַת הַמְּצֹרָע"

These are the laws of the leper (14:2)

Not far from the ancient city of Tzipori lived a peddler who made the rounds of the local markets in the surrounding towns and villages each day. He would advertise his wares by proclaiming, "Come and get your special potion to lengthen your life! Come and get the Elixir of Life! If you want a long life, come here and buy my wares."

Everyone came rushing to see what he had to sell.

Traveling from one town to another, the peddler once reached R' Yanai's city. Here, too, he set up his stand in the public square and proclaimed, "Who wants to live? Who wants a magic formula for long life? Come and buy my wares. I guarantee you long life."

R' Yanai, who was sitting at home learning Torah, suddenly, heard the peddler. Leaning out of the window, he said, "Won't you please come up here. I would, also, like to buy your marvelous medicine."

The peddler turned red with embarrassment. "My

merchandise is not for you, honored rabbi. You don't need my wares to gain long life. This is only for the common folk here."

"Nevertheless, I would like to see what you are selling there. Please come up."

The peddler declined, but R' Yanai insisted. Finally, he allowed himself to be persuaded by the sage and entered R' Yanai's home.

He unfastened his pack and withdrew a slim book, a copy of *Tehillim* which he opened to the verse, "Who is the man who desires life... guard your tongue from evil..." He explained, somewhat sheepishly, "This is the verse which I quote to all of my customers. I tell them that, if they desire a long life, they must guard their tongues from evil gossip, from *lashon hara*. This is the real secret prescription for a long life!"

"Right you are," said R' Yanai. "That is the medicine of life; that is what King David actually said: if a person guards himself from gossip and harmful speech, *Hashem* grants him long life. His son, King Shlomo, wisest of all men, also said the same thing but in other words: 'One who guards his mouth and tongue, protects himself from all harm.' "

(Adapted from Vayikra Rabbah 16:2)

Two Tongues

"זֹאת תִּהְיֶה תּוֹרַת הַמְצֹרָע"

These are the laws of the leper (14:2)

The leper — the evil gossiper

(Midrash Rabbah)

R' Shimon ben Gamliel had a servant, Tavi, who was a clever man. Once, R' Shimon sent his servant to the market and said, "Buy me some good food."

Tavi returned with a tongue which he had bought at the butcher's. R' Shimon thanked him, then he said, "Now buy me some bad food."

Soon Tavi returned bearing another tongue.

R' Shimon asked him, "Tell me, Tavi, how can tongue be both good food and bad food?"

"But that is the truth. A tongue can be both good and bad. When a tongue is good, nothing is better than it. When the tongue is bad, nothing is worse or more harmful than it."

How true this is — when a person uses his tongue for useful purposes — for studying Torah, praying, saying a kind word to a troubled person and the like, then his tongue is very good! But when a tongue is used for evil — for slandering, cursing, mocking, tale bearing and the like, then nothing is worse!

(Adapted from Vayikra Rabbah 33:1)

Tender, Soft Tongues

"זֹאת תִּהְיֶה תּוֹרַת הַמְּצֹרָע"

These are the laws of the leper (14:2)

The leper - the evil gossiper

(Midrash Rabbah)

R' Yehudah Hanasi, or Rebbe, as he was called, once wished to teach his students to mind their speech. Inviting them to a festive meal, he served them a delicacy, tongue. Some of the tongue was well cooked and soft while some was, purposely, undercooked and hard.

R' Yehudah Hanasi urged his *talmidim* to eat their fill but when the meal was over, the platters bearing the soft tongue were empty while those with the hard tongue were still full.

Pointing to the full platters, R' Yehudah said, "Take note of this, dear *talmidim*. All of you chose the soft tongue and left the undercooked, hard tongues untouched. This should be a lesson to you in life. You should always use a soft tongue, that is, you should always speak softly and kindly. Put aside a harsh tongue, words that are said in anger."

(Adapted from Vayikra Rabbah 33:1)

What Enters the Mouth and What Leaves it

"זאת תִּהְיֶה תּוֹרַת הַמְּצֹרָע"

These are the laws of the leper (14:2)

The leper — the evil gossiper

(Midrash Rabbah)

The Yehudi Hakadosh of Pshischa told his disciple, R' Simchah Bunim, to go on a journey, but he did not explain its purpose.

R' Simchah Bunim did not ask any questions, but gathered a few of the chasidim as traveling companions, and set out on their way.

They reached a small wayside inn run by a Jew. Here they stopped.

Not knowing the owner, the chasidim asked for a dairy supper.

"I am terribly sorry," the innkeeper apologized, "but I have nothing dairy to serve you. I can only offer meat."

The chasidim began cross-examining him. "Who is your *shochet*?"

"Who certified him to slaughter?"

"Does anyone inspect his knives periodically?"

"Who *kashered* the meat?"

"Were the animal's lungs carefully checked?"

"Was the meat properly rinsed after the salting?"

"Is it considered *glatt, mehadrin min hamehadrin*?"

Suddenly, a voice was heard from the corner. Everyone

looked and saw a shabbily dressed man sitting behind the stove. "Chasidim!" he said. "You have no end of questions. You wish to make sure that every single particular is perfectly kosher. You are so careful and meticulous about what goes into your mouths. Tell me, are you also as careful about what comes out of your mouths?"

R' Simchah Bunim realized that these must have been the words which his Rebbe had wanted him to hear; it was for this that he had been sent on a journey.

True Gossip

"זֹאת תִּהְיֶה תּוֹרַת הַמְּצֹרָע"

These are the laws of the leper (14:2)

The leper — the evil gossiper

(Midrash Rabbah)

A group of Jews were once standing around on a street corner in Berditchov, whiling away the time with idle gossip. R' Levi Yitzchak, their rabbi, came by. He greeted them pleasantly and asked, "And what are you talking about?"

One of them, a man with a clever and sharp tongue, replied, "We were bored. To while away the time we indulged in a bit of gossip about our fellow townspeople. But don't worry, we didn't say any lies. We spoke the honest truth."

R' Levi Yitzchak spoke sadly, "Our Sages teach us that *Hashem* also wears *tefillin*, but they are not like ours. His *tefillin* say: 'Who is like Your nation Yisrael, (they are) a unique people in the land.' By speaking *lashon hara* about your fellow Jew, even if it be the truth, you are slandering the truth of of the Creator's *tefillin*!"

The Afflictions of the House

"וְהִגִּיד לַכֹּהֵן לֵאמֹר כְּנֶגַע נִרְאָה לִי בַּבָּיִת"

And he shall tell the kohen saying, such a lesion appeared to me in the house (14:35)

R' Mordechai of Pinchov did not have two pennies to rub together. Small wonder, then, that his wife would beg him, whenever he went to his Rebbe, the Chozeh of Lublin, to speak of their sorry plight and ask for advice and a blessing. But as soon as he entered the Rebbe's room, the world of here and now vanished. He forgot all about his wife's pleas and had only eyes and ears for the Rebbe. They would spend hours in exploring the intricacies of Torah, the Talmud and Chasidus. All worldly things were as mere shadows compared to their eternal wisdom.

And so R' Mordechai returned to Pinchov each time invigorated in spirit. He glowed. But when he entered the house and his wife greeted him with the question, "Well, did you speak to the Rebbe about *parnasah* this time?" R' Mordechai would strike his forehead. He had completely forgotten again!

When they had sold everything they possibly could and were down to their last crust, she again came crying to R' Mordechai, "You must go to the Chozeh again. You must beg him to pray for us. This time, however, I want to make sure that you do not forget. *I* will accompany you!"

And indeed, the next time he visited Lublin, he entered the Rebbe's study and blurted out the words immediately, before they could slip his mind, "Rebbe! I can bear it no longer." He went on to describe the squalor and poverty in his home, begging the Rebbe to pray for him.

"I did not realize that things were so bad. Why did you never mention this to me before!" he said in a note of complaint. "You should not have allowed things to reach such a terrible state!"

R' Mordechai hung his head in shame. "I felt it was not right to bother the Rebbe with material matters. Besides," he added, lowering his voice, "I always thought that, in his divine intuition, the Rebbe would know of my condition."

The Chozeh smiled and said, "The Torah differentiates between leprosy upon a person and leprosy that afflicts a house. With regards to a person it says, 'And if a man has on his skin a leprous lesion... and the *kohen* shall see the spots (*Vayikra 13 2-3).*' This implies that a person need not tell the *kohen* what happened. It is enough to come to the *kohen*. He will see it without your telling him and know what to do.

In contrast, with regard to plague spots on the walls of

a house, the Torah states: 'And the owner of the house shall come and tell the *kohen* thus: such a spot did I see in my house.' The Torah explicitly states that in connection with things that concern the house one must tell the *kohen* exactly what is wrong with the house, before he can begin to treat it."

A Short Prayer

"וְלֹא יִטְמָא כָּל-אֲשֶׁר בַּבָּיִת"

And all that is in the house will not become impure (14:36)

The Torah tried to spare earthenware vessels which cannot
be purified in a mikveh

(Rashi)

When R' Yisrael Salanter passed through Warsaw, he went to pay his respects to the Gerrer Rebbe, the Chidushei Harim. The latter showed his great deference and at the end of the visit accompanied his guest to the street.

The chasidim of the Rebbe heard of this and, when R' Yisrael went to a nearby *shul* for *minchah*, he drew a huge crowd after him.

All watched R' Yisrael carefully as he prayed. R' Yisrael did not pray at length, as did other outstanding sages; he prayed briefly like an ordinary Jew.

When he took the required three steps signifying the end of the *shemoneh esreh* prayer, R' Yisrael turned around to see everyone staring at him.

"You are probably wondering why I was so quick about my prayers. I noticed that many left their work because of my presence, here. The blacksmith left his forge, the shoemaker his last, the carpenter his workbench and the tailor his needle. Had I prayed at length, I would have caused Jews to lose time and money."

Isolation and Discovery

"וְאַרְבָּעָה אֲנָשִׁים הָיוּ מְצֹרָעִים פֶּתַח הַשָּׁעַר"

There were four men, lepers, at the gateway
(Haftorah Parashas Metzora, Melachim II 7:3)

It was the year 5608 (1848). The city of Vilna was in the grips of a terrible epidemic. The killer cholera was sweeping through the city and the surrounding countryside and the Jewish community was in a turmoil. As in all times of trouble, Jews gathered to pray to *Hashem*. Their leaders exhorted them to search their hearts and repent, each one for his particular sins. People were urged to give charity and be especially kind to one another.

Most people genuinely repented and improved. There were some, however, who instead of examining their own faults and sins, eagerly examined those of their neighbors.

One such Jew came to R' Yisrael Salanter during this time. He had something to confess. He whispered in the rabbi's ear of some sin he saw in a fellow Jew.

"Rabbi, who knows if it is not that very sin which is causing our plague? Something must be done about that person," he said.

As usual, R' Yisrael listened patiently and when his visitor fell silent, he said, "As you know, the Torah instructs us to send the leper from all three camps (of the *kohanim, leviim* and the rest of the people, Yisrael). Our Sages tell us that leprosy is the punishment sent upon a tale-bearer, the *baal lashon hara*. Some people think that this sin only applies to lies one says about another. That is not so. A person who searches out other people's faults and sins is certainly considered a *baal lashon hara*, too. We tell him, 'If you think that you are expert at discovering sins, go out of the camp. There, where you will be isolated for many days, you won't be able to uncover another's sins. But you will certainly be able to discover and see your own.'"

פָּרָשַׁת אַחֲרֵי מוֹת

Parashas Acharei Mos

The Empty Glass

"וּבָא אַהֲרֹן אֶל אֹהֶל מוֹעֵד"

And Aharon will come to Ohel Moed (16:23)

...to remove the spoon and the fire-pan.

(Rashi)

R' Yitzchak of Drohovitz, father of the famous R' Yechiel Michel of Zolotchov, was among the original disciples of the Baal Shem Tov and, actually, attended the Father of Chasidus for a period in his life.

Once, the Baal Shem Tov asked for a glass of tea. In those days R' Yitzchak served him and waited patiently behind him, until the Baal Shem had finished drinking. He, then, took the empty glass and returned it to its proper place.

The Baal Shem Tov smiled at him and said, "I am sure that when you brought me the tea, you did so with the intention of serving a Torah scholar. Tell me, though, why did you wait all this time to take the empty glass away?"

R' Yitzchak humbly explained, "In the time of the *Beis Hamikdash*, on *Yom Kippur*, the *Kohen Gadol* was required to enter the Holy of Holies two times, once in the morning bearing the spoon and fire-pan for the sacrifice of the incense, *ketores*, and the second time, in the late afternoon, to remove these vessels. Certainly, the *Kohen Gadol* went in the second time, to remove these holy objects, with no less reverence and sanctity than with which he had brought them!"

A Gold Coin to Cover the Blood

"וְשָׁפַךְ אֶת דָּמוֹ וְכִסָּהוּ בֶּעָפָר"

He shall spill its blood and cover it with earth (17:13)

R' Baruch Zeldowitz of Minsk was a prominent and respected figure. Throughout Lithuania and Russia, wherever there was a *yeshivah*, his name was a household word. R' Baruch was a wealthy businessman who, not only supported dozens of Torah institutions but, was a scholar in his own right. He devoted time each day for his Torah studies, without fail. He was, also, known as a generous man; his house was open to all, for money, meals and lodging.

R' Baruch never turned anyone away without a generous donation. But there was one cause that was particularly dear to his heart — the Volozhiner Yeshivah. Each year he gave a handsome gift to the *yeshivah* where he had learned in his youth.

R' Baruch was sitting in his office one day, deeply involved in a complex business deal which, if handled properly, would bring in great profits. Suddenly, an elderly man burst into the office. Rudely interrupting the negotiations and without an apology, he said, "I have come from the Volozhiner Yeshivah. I have come to collect your annual donation."

R' Baruch was taken aback. "Pardon me, sir, but do you have an appointment? Why didn't you knock before coming in, as decent manners demand?"

As soon as R' Baruch had begun in his scolding tone, the man had lowered his eyes and bowed his head, blushing with embarrassment. He sheepishly shuffled out of the room.

Some time later the two men leaned back in their chairs, mutually satisfied with the terms of the deal they had drawn up. The visitor rose, stretched out a hand to R' Baruch to seal their agreement, then left the room. R' Baruch suddenly remembered that the collector from the *yeshivah* was still waiting outside. He recalled his recent outburst with shame. He had certainly hurt the man and embarrassed him deeply. Perhaps he could set things aright.

He went to the door and called the man in and asked him to sit down. "I must apologize for my behavior. The *gemara* in *Chulin* says that blood must be covered by earth (after the slaughter of a fowl or wild animal) but that gold dust many be used instead, because gold is also considered earth, as it says, 'And the earth of gold is his.'"

With these words, he took out a gold coin from his purse and pressed it into the man's hand, explaining, "Just a short while ago, I was guilty of shedding blood, that is, embarrassing you, which the Torah equates with murder. I am, therefore, required to cover up this blood. Please accept this gold coin together with my apologies. And don't think that I am deducting it from my yearly contribution. That will remain the same. I am forever indebted to the Volozhiner Yeshivah for that is where I learned in my youth."

The Feast that Brought Destruction

"וְלֹא תָקִיא הָאָרֶץ אֶתְכֶם בְּטַמַּאֲכֶם אֹתָה"

So that the land shall not vomit you forth when you defile it (18:28)

When the *Beis Hamikdash* still stood in all of its glory, a man once held a grand party. He made up a guest list of all the friends whom he wished to join him and had his servant invite them personally.

The servant made his rounds, checking off name after name, until he reached the home of Kamtza — a close friend of his master. But the servant had his mind on other matters and, mistakenly, invited not Kamtza, but Bar Kamtza, little realizing that this man was on bad terms with his master.

Bar Kamtza accepted the invitation and, disregarding

past differences, decided to attend the party of his former enemy.

When the appointed day arrived, Bar Kamtza came and took a seat at one of the tables. The host circulated among the guests, welcoming them and thanking them for having come. When he drew up before Bar Kamtza, his expression changed. He became red with anger and shouted, "And who invited *you* to the party? Since when have you considered me your friend? Get out immediately! I don't want to see your face in my house!"

Bar Kamtza was taken by surprise. This was hardly what he had expected. "I am here already," he said pleadingly. "Please let me stay. Don't embarrass me in front of all these distinguished people. I will pay for what I eat. Just don't throw me out now."

The host was livid with rage. "Out, I said. You are no friend of mine! I didn't invite you and I don't want you to stay in my house one minute longer."

Bar Kamtza cringed. He felt all eyes turned on him. He wished he could sink into the ground. But, there was the host, shaking his fist at him. "Please," he managed to whisper. "I will pay for half of this party. For all of it, even, if you want. But don't embarrass me in front of all these important people."

"Do you think I need your money? Out! Out! This very minute!"

Other guests had arrived by now. This scene was the focus of all attention. The host was beside himself with rage. Gasping for breath, he ran up to Bar Kamtza, grabbed him by the robe, dragged him to the door and threw him out.

Embarrassed, hurt and angry, Bar Kamtza stood at the door. What a disgrace! He would never live it down.

Everyone had been there; the town's most distinguished scholars and citizens. Everyone had seen him being thrown out. And no one had even opened his mouth to defend him. No one had put in a good word for him.

"I cannot let this go by. I must avenge myself upon that hateful man and upon all of those guests," he thought.

Bar Kamtza went directly to Rome, which then ruled *Eretz Yisrael* and told the emperor that the Jews were planning to rebel. The emperor listened to him and asked for proof.

"Send a peace offering to the Jews, a sacrifice for their Temple. If they are planning to rebel against you, they will reject it."

The emperor selected a fine bull, a magnificent perfect animal without a single blemish, as a gesture of good will to the Jews. Bar Kamtza promised to bring it to the *Beis Hamikdash*. While transporting the animal, he made a small cut in one of the animal's lips. It was not noticeable to the casual eye and to the Romans it would surely not have been considered a blemish. But when the *kohanim* examined the animal and saw it, they had to reject it.

When the king learned that his gift had not been accepted as worthy enough for the Temple, he believed Bar Kamtza's evil slander. He sent an immense army to capture Jerusalem. It was this army that destroyed the holy city and burned down the *Beis Hamikdash*.

All because of false pride...

(Adapted from Tractate Gittin 55-6)

The Cruel King's Bitter End

"עֵינֵי ה' בַּמַּמְלָכָה הַחַטָּאָה וְהִשְׁמַדְתִּי אֹתָהּ"

*The eyes of Hashem are on the sinful kingdom and I will
destroy it*
(Haftorah Parashas Acharei Mos, Amos 9:8)

Titus, the wicked king who destroyed the holy city of
Jerusalem and burned down the *Beis Hamikdash*,
gloried in his victory. He gathered all the holy gold and
silver vessels and loaded them upon many ships to take
back to Rome. He also took many Jewish captives to be
sold as slaves. How proud he was of himself! This nation
had been considered invincible, unconquerable! And he,
the mighty Titus, had subdued them utterly. The Jews
were now his slaves and their magnificent Temple was
razed to the ground.

Little did this arrogant king realize that he was a mere
tool, a pawn in the hands of the A-mighty, a whip to
punish the Jews for their sins. All his power came only
from *Hashem*.

Titus did not understand this. He boasted and cursed
the Jewish G-d. And *Hashem* became angry.

As Titus was traveling home, a fierce storm suddenly
broke out at sea. His sturdy ship was tossed about like a
nutshell. Huge waves threatened to smash it. But Titus
was undaunted. Standing on the deck, he shouted up to
the sky, "I am not afraid of you, *Hashem*! All of your
power is only on water. Why was I able to conquer your
people, the Jews? How was I able to destroy your
Temple? Because all of your strength is only on the sea.

You brought a great flood to destroy the world. You drowned the Egyptians in the Red Sea. But, on land I am supreme. I challenge you to meet me on my battleground, on land. Then we will see who is the mighty one!"

"Wicked man! Fool!" said *Hashem*. "As soon as you step on land I will send one of My smallest creatures on earth to punish you."

The sea was calm; the ship sped over the Mediterranean on its way to Rome. And then it docked at port, bearing the conquering hero.

Music blared, soldiers saluted smartly, flags waved as the ship slid into the harbor and Titus disembarked. He was greeted by his ministers who placed a crown on his head and gave him some vintage wine in a golden goblet. Just as Titus lifted the goblet to his lips a tiny mosquito flew up his nose.

He sneezed, but the insect was not dislodged. It had penetrated through his nose into the sinus cavity and entered straight into his head! There it went to work, droning away, eating at Titus' brain.

Titus suffered from terrible headaches. Nothing alleviated the pain. The buzzing in his brain never ceased as the tiny mosquito gnawed away. One day, Titus was driving through the city streets when he passed by a blacksmith's shop. The hammer beat against metal on the anvil. The pounding of metal on metal was deafening. The mosquito was silenced and the constant buzzing in Titus' head ceased.

He was overjoyed and ordered the blacksmith to the palace to pound away so that he might get some rest. But, with the passage of time, the mosquito grew accustomed to the noise and resumed its gnawing and buzzing. Titus continued to suffer for the next seven

years, day and night. He became weaker and weaker until he was a mere shadow. His strength played out; he could no longer bear his suffering and died. After his death they opened the skull and found a creature that had the shape of a mosquito, but was the size of a pigeon!

(Adapted from Tractate Gittin 56b; Bereishis Rabbah 10:7)

פָּרָשַׁת קְדוֹשִׁים

Parashas Kedoshim

Not the Half As Yet

"אִישׁ אִמּוֹ וְאָבִיו תִּירָאוּ"

Fear your mother and father (19:3)

The requirement to be holy does not apply only to special, exalted people. Rather: "Speak to the entire community of Yisrael... (and exhort them to) be sanctified." This teaches us that every single Jew is capable and obligated to reach the level of sanctity.

The famous *tana*, R' Tarfon, was one of the wealthiest persons of his time. He had an immense home with numerous servants who cleaned and polished, cooked and served and kept everything in perfect order.

There was one thing, however, which he did not allow them to do. That was to serve his elderly mother. R' Tarfon's mother lived with him. She had her own room with a high bed. It was difficult for her to climb in and out of the bed and, whenever she wished to do so, he would bend low, so that she could use his back as a footstool.

It was a lovely spring *Shabbos*. R' Tarfon's mother took a stroll in the garden. Suddenly the strap of her shoe tore. She stopped. It was forbidden to make even a temporary repair; it was *Shabbos*. Nor could she return barefoot. The ground was still cold and damp. She was too frail and delicate. She would certainly catch cold and at her age that was dangerous. She looked around for help, when, there was her son, R' Tarfon, at her side. He had seen his mother standing motionless and had come.

Before she could stop him, R' Tarfon had bent down and placed his two hands under his mother's foot so that she could take a step. Right foot, left foot. At each step R' Tarfon was ready with his two hands held out to support his mother's foot so that it would not touch the ground. The two walked thus, step after painstaking step, until they finally reached the house. R' Tarfon, the wealthy scholar, the great *tana* did not think of his own honor. He was not embarrassed. No indeed! He was proud to be able to serve his mother!

Some time later R' Tarfon became ill. His friends, the other Sages, came to visit him. When she saw those distinguished guests, the elderly mother rushed over to them. She thanked them for coming, then, with tears in her eyes, begged them fervently to pray for her son, Tarfon.

"He is such a good son! He shows me such respect. You must pray for him that he live. He deserves to, if just on the merit of his *kibud em*, his deep respect for me. After all, the Torah states that the reward for showing parental respect is long life!"

The Sages were curious to hear how R' Tarfon expressed his respect. The old woman told them all the things her son did.

They listened respectfully, then said, "Fine! That is admirable. Still, were he to do even a million times more he would not even reach half of what the Torah obliges him to do for you!"

(One explanation of this is that the Sages said this not to belittle his parental respect, but to indicate that R' Tarfon had not yet completed his task on this world. He still had a task to perform on earth and should live to reach still greater heights in fulfilling the *mitzvah* of *kibud em*).

(According to Tractate *Kidushin 31b; Yerushalmi Kidushin Perek 1*)

The Valuable Letter

"לֹא תִּגְנֹבוּ"

You shall not steal (19:11)

It was Sunday morning, the beginning of a new week. Yosel's belongings were all packed and he was ready to leave. Today, the gentile day of rest, would not be too profitable for this traveling peddler from Leipnik. He heaved a deep sigh. He was already tired, even before he had lifted his heavy knapsack. How would he feel at the end of the week?! He was not getting any younger. Still, he made a few pennies each week. His family had not starved yet.

He had one foot out of the door and turned around to say good-by to his wife when he looked at her and stopped.

"What is the matter? Why do you look so sad?" he asked.

Gittel burst into tears. "I can't help crying," she sobbed. "It is so difficult to make ends meet. I know that you work hard. I know it is not your fault. Still, I cannot help crying and worrying."

"Well, don't fret. Perhaps *Hashem* will have pity on us and will send Eliyahu Hanavi to release us from our troubles." He smiled encouragingly and left the house, closing the door softly.

He began walking along the road, humming a sad tune, when the mail coach flew by. Two letters fluttered in the wind and came to rest at Yosel's feet. He picked them up. One was a registered letter. The postal markings on it indicated that it contained thirty thousand marks. The other was an ordinary letter.

Instinctively, Yosel thrust the first letter inside his shirt. Waving the second letter, he shouted to the coach to stop.

"Hey there! You lost a letter! Stop, wait! You lost a letter!"

The driver reined the horses to a halt. Yosel came running up. "Here! This letter must have blown out of the mail pouch. Take it!"

The driver took the letter, thanked Yosel, flicked the reins over the horses' backs and the mail coach was soon out of sight.

Yosel stood in thought for a short while. What should he do, now that Eliyahu Hanavi had answered his prayers and sent him thirty thousand marks? It was pointless to continue on his way and sweat all week long for a few copper pennies! And so, he slung his knapsack over his back and headed back home.

Gittel was alarmed to see her husband back so soon. "What is the matter?" she asked.

"Our prayers have been answered!" he said, telling her all about the letter which had fallen at his very feet.

But Gittel was not at all enthusiastic. On the contrary, she was frightened. "How could you have taken the money? It does not belong to you! You stole it! Have you become a thief? Is that how low we have fallen?!"

Yosel tried to calm her. "I am certain that the owner of the money will hardly miss the thirty thousand marks. He is probably a wealthy man with millions. He can spare that much. Besides, the post office will refund it to him. And, I could tell from the names that the sender and the addressee were not Jewish. Why the fuss? Don't worry about it. It will be alright."

Gittel was determined to have the last word. "Stealing is stealing, no matter what you say. What will our children say tomorrow when they wake up to learn that their parents have become thieves?"

Yossel pretended he had not heard. He stubbornly insisted that he had the right to keep what he had found. He certainly had no intention of returning the letter.

But Gittel had not resigned herself. "The post office officials will probably come here tomorrow. They know that you found one letter; they will think of looking here for the second one too."

These words had an effect upon Yosel, but not the desired one. Instead of taking the letter to the post office immediately, he went over to a large wooden wardrobe which stood against the wall. He pushed it aside, pried up a floor board, hid the money underneath, then shoved the closet back into place. Nothing looked amiss.

Gittel had been perfectly right. A few hours later two men appeared at the door. They were the post office manager and a policeman.

"Did you find another letter besides the one you returned?" they asked Yosel.

"No!" Yosel brazenly lied. The letter he had returned had been the only one he had seen.

The postal manager turned to the policeman and said, "I think he is telling the truth. I know Yosel; he is an honest man. If he has stolen the letter, why would he have troubled to return the other one? No, Yosel has an excellent reputation in town."

The policeman, however, suspected that the mailcoach driver and the Jew had connived to steal the letter together. The story was very suspicious. Although he did not have any evidence to go on, he imprisoned both the driver and the Jew.

When the townspeople heard that Yosel the peddler had been put into jail, they came to Gittel to offer their sympathy. "We know that he is innocent," people told her. "Yosel is an honest man. He would not have stolen the letter. Just wait and see; he will be proven innocent."

These reassurances were like daggers in Gittel's heart. She knew that her husband *had* taken the money! He had been justly thrown into prison.

Meanwhile the police were conducting an extensive investigation. The postal authorities offered a large reward to anyone who returned the missing letter. But, obviously, no one returned the letter.

Yosel remained in jail. There was no one to prove him innocent and so, he was considered guilty.

Gittel saw that the situation showed no signs of improvement and decided to take the matter into her own hands. With iron determination and more than human power, she moved the heavy wooden closet. She lifted the floor boards and withdrew the letter that had brought so much misfortune upon them. She could not return it to the post office or to the police, for then her husband would certainly be incriminated. She would put the letter, and the problem, in the rabbi's lap. In his great wisdom R' Baruch Frankel-Teumim would know what to do.

She went right off to the rabbi. When she drew near his home, she heard him teaching a group of *talmidim*. She was certainly not going to burst into his room and make a public confession. The letter seemed to her to be burning in her hand; she did not want to hold on to it a moment longer. Impulsively, she threw it through an open window and returned swiftly home. Now the problem was out of her hands.

R' Baruch Frankel-Teumim was sitting by his table, deeply engrossed in the lesson, when, suddenly, something white flew in from the window and came to rest on the floor by his chair. He bent down to pick it up. It was a letter. It bore an offical stamp declaring that this was a registered letter containing thirty thousand marks. Suddenly, he realized that this must be the missing — or stolen — letter. What should he do?

R' Baruch dismissed his *talmidim* and sat down to think. If he went to authorities and handed in the letter, they would immediately suspect him and his community of being criminally involved. No one would believe that the rabbi had 'found' it. Public pressure, they would say, had made them change their minds about keeping the money. This would cause a terrible *chillul Hashem*.

No. That was not the answer.

He had no ready solution and temporarily hid the letter in his drawer.

But this made him very uneasy and a few minutes later

he changed his mind. "No, that was the wrong thing to do," he thought. "Perhaps someone threw the letter into my room in order to implicate the Jewish community. The police would make a search here and would find the planted letter." R' Baruch put the letter back on the floor, exactly where he had found it, and left the house. If the police came, meanwhile, to search, they would see that the letter had been thrown in through the window.

R' Baruch went for a walk. He had to clear his mind in order to think this problem through. Sunk deep in thought, the rabbi walked, not looking where his feet were taking him. A while later he found himself beyond the city, walking along a deserted road.

The local priest was also out, taking a stroll. The two men knew each other quite well. The priest regarded the rabbi highly, knowing him to be a holy man. When he saw R' Baruch approaching, his eyes lit up and he rushed forward to greet him. He could not help noticing how troubled the rabbi looked.

"Good afternoon, Rabbi!" he said. "I see that something is bothering you. You look very distressed. Would it help to talk it over with someone?" he continued kindly.

R' Baruch looked up and saw his acquaintance. A strange idea struck him. He returned the greeting, then asked, "Is it not true that you priests are required to keep confessions a secret?"

The priest nodded. Everyone knew that. "In the Christian religion, confessions are strictly confidential."

"And are you permitted to hear confessions from people who are not members of your faith?"

"Yes."

"Very well, then," said the rabbi, "I have something to confess to you but I wish to do so in the privacy of your own home. And I want this to be strictly confidential, like all of your other confessions."

The priest looked into the rabbi's eyes to see if he was joking. But no, he was deadly serious. "Very well. You may come to my house. I even have a special confessional booth."

"That will not be necessary," said R' Baruch. "All I need is absolute secrecy. When can I come?"

The priest and he agreed on a time.

R' Baruch Frankel went home, took the letter which rested on the floor, untouched, and returned to the priest's house. There he poured out his strange story.

"I am very confused. I don't know what to do! The only thing I can think of is to give the letter to you. You can hand it over to the authorities."

"But what shall I say? How shall I explain my possession of the letter?"

"You can say that you received it during confession but that you are not at liberty to say who gave it to you. I am sure that the police will not ask any further questions."

The priest agreed that this was the best solution.

The news broke the following day. Within the hour everyone in town knew that the missing letter had been found. Yosel was exonerated and released from jail with a sincere apology for his having been falsely suspected.

Yosel returned home. When Gittel confessed what she had done, he agreed that she had done the right thing. And when she told him that he must rush to the rabbi and confess his guilt, he did not protest. Gittel had been right since the very beginning; she was probably right now too. He would have to go, painful though the confession would be.

Yosel received a royal welcome at the rabbi's house.

"Blessed is *Hashem* Who releases prisoners!" R' Baruch said warmly, happy to see Yosel. "Thank G-d that you were proven innocent and that justice has prevailed!"

To his surprise, Yosel burst into tears. The rabbi closed the door and sat him down. "Tell me, what is bothering you."

Yosel confessed, "I am not innocent at all! I am the one who stole the money! I am the guilty culprit! I am a terrible sinner!"

He now told the rabbi the entire story, from beginning to end, concluding, "I regret my foolishness. I should never have given in to temptation." Yosel wiped the tears from his eyes and waited, head bowed, to hear what the rabbi had to say.

The rabbi began comforting him. Suddenly there was a knock at the door. The priest entered, bearing a note of five hundred marks.

"This is the reward money," he said to R' Baruch. "It belongs to you. You found the missing letter."

"Oh no!" the rabbi shook his head. "I cannot take it. The money is yours. You deserve it since you are the one who gave back the money."

"But I did not find the money. If you do not want it, at least accept it and distribute this prize amongst the poor."

The rabbi shook his head. "No, I can't do that either for the credit is still yours. Wait... I have an idea." He looked at Yosel. "Here is poor Yosel who sat in jail and suffered, all because of that letter. I think it fitting that he get the reward. Besides, he is very poor and can surely use the money."

The priest nodded. "That is the perfect solution. Why didn't I think of it myself? Yosel surely deserves the prize!"

But Yosel did not want to hear of it. His conscience was still bothering him for having taken the letter to begin with. But after the rabbi insisted, he finally accepted it.

"Now you can open up a business," R' Baruch advised. "You need not continue traveling and eking out a difficult living. With a shop, you will earn much more and be able to support your family in comfort."

Yosel listened to the rabbi's advice. And R' Baruch's blessing helped him prosper until in a short time he became rich. Yosel never forgot his days of poverty. He gave charity with a generous hand for the rest of his life.

The Little Genius

"לֹא תִּגְנֹבוּ"

You shall not steal (19:11)

This is a warning to the thief. "Thou shalt not steal" in the Ten Commandments refers to kidnapping (not the theft of money).

(Rashi)

A peasant once entered the central synagogue of Volozhin to pray. He had brought along his own *siddur*. When he finished praying, he put it down on the table and turned to greet someone he knew. The two men talked for a few minutes, then the peasant turned to go. He looked around for his *siddur,* but could not find it.

"Where did it go?" he muttered to himself. He went from one table to another, thinking that, perhaps, someone had taken it by mistake and mislaid it elsewhere. He looked high and low but the *siddur* had vanished.

Had someone taken it? The villager looked around the synagogue for the guilty one. He spied a young child studying in the corner. "Aha! That must be the one! He must have taken a fancy to my *siddur* and taken it!"

Little Zalman, who would later grow up to be R' Shlomo Zalman of Volozhin, one of the prominent disciples of the Vilna Gaon, showed promise, even at the age of five.

The villager turned to an old man next to him and said in a loud whisper, "Do you see that child there? He probably took it."

The old man, who knew Zalman well and already respected him highly, frowned and said angrily, "Shhhhh! Do you know whom you are talking about? That is Zalman, our child prodigy. He is a genius already, even at the age of five! We expect great things of him! He is the pride of our community — and you suspect him of committing the sin of *'lo signov* — thou shalt not steal?!"

Before the visitor even had a chance to react, a childish voice piped up from the corner, "Even if I had taken the *siddur,* which I have not, I would not be guilty of *lo signov!*"

Everyone's attention was focused upon the scene. Eyebrows lifted at this strange statement of the little genius. How was taking someone else's possession not considered stealing?!

The childish voice piped up again. "The Torah forbids stealing in the Ten Commandments and, again, in *Vayikra.*

Rashi explains that *lo signovu* in Vayikra refers to stealing money and possessions, while the *lo signov* of the Ten Commandments refers to kidnapping!

"And so," he concluded in his clear voice, "had I taken this man's *siddur* I would have been guilty of *lo signovu* — You shall not steal — and not *lo signov* — Thou shalt not steal."

The Deceptive Clouds

"וְלֹא־תְשַׁקְּרוּ אִישׁ בַּעֲמִיתוֹ"
You shall not lie to one another (19:11)

When the great scholar Ula arrived in Bavel, the weather, suddenly, became stormy. Black clouds filled the sky and thunder rumbled in the distance.

"Quick, bring all the things into the house. There is going to be a thunderstorm and everything will be ruined!" he urged the people.

They did as Ula said. But not a drop fell. The thick clouds dispersed and a clear blue sky reappeared!

Everyone was surprised. Surely rain should have fallen. The only one who was not amazed was Ula.

He called the people together and said, "You all expected rain to fall. Do you know why it did not? It is a sign from heaven. A direct reflection in nature of your own behavior. You lie and cheat, you are false to one another. Thus nature also cheats and deceives you. You thought that rain was going to fall but you were deceived — just as you deceive one another!"

(Adapted from Tractate Taanis 9b)

The Coin in the Flour Barrel

"וְלֹא תִשָּׁבְעוּ בִשְׁמִי לַשָּׁקֶר"

You shall not swear falsely in My Name (19:12)

One should not even swear upon something true...
(Tanchumah, Vayikra 7)

A man once had a gold coin which he deposited with his neighbor, a widow. The woman put it into a flour barrel and forgot all about it.

Once, she scooped out some flour with the coin in it and baked it in a bread. She gave the bread to a poor man who came to the door, not realizing, that the loaf contained her neighbor's gold coin.

Time passed and the man came to claim his coin.

She had forgotten all about it. She did not even remember having received it. She was certain that she had not taken it and said that she was ready to take an oath to that effect.

"I swear that the coin is not in my possession and that I never had any benefit from it! And if what I say is false, let one of my sons die!"

Before long, one of her sons died.

When the Sages heard what had happened, they said, "If this is what happens to a woman who swore to something true — as she did — who knows what will happen to someone who swears falsely!"

(Adapted from Tractate Gittin 35a)

The Man Who Trembled

"לֹא־תַעֲשׂוּ עָוֶל בַּמִּשְׁפָּט"

You shall not do injustice in judgment (19:15)

The city of Kidan was split in two. One camp sided with the local *shochet*, while the other was against him. The situation became more heated from day to day. Something had to be done. Some good people in Kidon suggested that R' Eliyahu Levinsohn from Kartinga, a rabbi known for his peace-loving character and great scholarship, be asked to settle the problem and restore peace to their city.

R' Eliyahu suggested that the *shochet* be brought before two well known rabbis, whom he recommended, to be tested in the laws of *shechitah*.

The decisive day arrived. A long table had been set up for the two rabbis, filled with drinks, luscious fruit and tempting cakes and pastry. They sat there, partaking of the refreshments, while the *shochet* stood by, trembling, waiting for the test to begin.

"We would like to see your slaughtering knife," the rabbis said to the man. His hands shaking with fear, the *shochet* took out his knife and began sharpening it. But he was so frightened that he ruined the edge. The knife that he presented for the rabbis' inspection had a fault and did not meet with their approval.

R' Eliyahu sat nearby. He could no longer contain himself. "Put that knife down and sit at the table," he said to the *shochet*. Meekly, the *shochet* did as he was told. R' Eliyahu put a platter of cakes and a glass of tea in front of him and coaxed him to eat. Slowly the man began to relax. When R' Eliyahu saw that his hands no longer trembled, he said, "Now try again. Take the knife and sharpen it properly."

The *shochet* took his stone, sharpened the slaughtering knife and then presented it to the two rabbis for inspection. They looked it over carefully, running their nail over the edge. It was perfectly smooth. It even cut a hair. They nodded their approval. The *shochet* had passed the test.

Without any further ado, they awarded him a certificate as a proper *shochet*.

Judging Favorably

"בְּצֶדֶק תִּשְׁפֹּט עֲמִיתֶךָ"
You shall judge your comrade righteously (19:15)

There was a poor man who lived in a village in the north of *Eretz Yisrael* at the time that the *Beis Hamikdash* stood. He could not find work to support his family.

"I will go south," he thought. "There the land is much more fertile. There are wealthy landowners with large farms in the south. I will work there and, when I have earned enough money, I will return home."

The man left his village and started walking

southward. He walked for many days until he reached the southern part of the country. There he found work with a wealthy farmer. He did his work well and diligently, from morning to night. The farmer was pleased.

He worked hard for three years. Not once did he go up north for a visit, for his home was too far away.

The three years passed. He wanted to go home. He waited eagerly for *Rosh Hashanah* to pass, so that he might begin his journey. He wished to be home for *Succos*.

He went to his master for his wages. "I wish to return home for *Succos*," he explained.

The master frowned. "I cannot pay you. I have no money."

The laborer did not understand. Here was a flourishing farm that had just produced a bountiful harvest. What did he mean that he had no money to pay? Perhaps, the farmer did not have cash. "I will accept payment in fruit, if you have no money," the worker offered.

"I have no fruit."

"Perhaps you can sell a field and pay me."

"I do not own any fields.," said the master.

"Then give me animals," he suggested.

"I have no animals to give you."

The worker was crestfallen. "Give me some quilts and pillows. It is very cold up north. It even snows in the winter. My children will be very happy with warm feather quilts."

The farmer didn't look at him. He turned his face aside and said, "I have no quilts or pillows to give you."

Crestfallen, the worker packed his few belongings and headed homeward. He had worked for three years, from morning to night, with nothing to show for it. Nothing! He was returning home emptyhanded. But he did not complain. He thought, "My master is a good man. If he says that he has nothing to give me, there must be a reason."

The man returned to his village with empty hands.

Succos passed. One morning, the laborer noticed a cloud of dust down the road; a caravan was approaching. A man was leading many pack animals loaded with sacks and barrels. To his amazement, that man was his former master, the wealthy farmer from the south.

The laborer rushed out to greet him and invited him into his home.

"First I wish to unpack the animals," the man said. "Everything you see here, the barrels of wine, sacks of flour, the fruits — everything is yours."

The farmer then handed him a purse full of coins. "And these are your wages for three years. Tell me," he asked the bewildered laborer, "what did you think when I said that I could not pay you in cash?"

"Why, I thought that perhaps you suddenly were offered an excellent bargain in merchandise and used all of your ready money to buy it up."

"And when you asked for fruit and I refused, saying that I had none, what did you think?"

The laborer answered, "I thought that you had not yet taken the *maaser*. Thus, you could not give me any."

"When you suggested that I sell a field in order to pay you, and I refused, what did you think then?"

"I thought that, perhaps, you had already arranged to rent your fields to someone and could not break your agreement by selling them."

"When you offered to take animals instead of money, I

said that I had none. What did you think then?"

"There, again, I thought that you had lent or leased them to someone."

"You were willing to take quilts and pillows, but I said I had none. What did you imagine then?"

"I thought that, perhaps, you had vowed to give your possessions to the *Beis Hamikdash*. Thus, you had nothing to give me."

The rich farmer nodded, beaming, "You were completely right! That is exactly what happened. You see, my son refused to study Torah. I was so disturbed about it that I swore that I would give all of my possessions to the *Beis Hamikdash* rather than let him inherit it. But, then I had my regrets. I went to the Sages and begged them to absolve me of this vow. They found a way to annul my vow. I, immediately, took your wages and made my way here. And now I have paid what I owe. I must return home now, but before I do, I would like to bless you, 'May *Hashem* always judge you favorably, just as you judged me favorably!'"

(Adapted from Tractate Shabbos 127b and Yalkut Shimoni 611)

Sons of the Living G-d

"לֹא תֵלֵךְ רָכִיל בְּעַמֶּיךָ"
You shall not bear gossip among your people (19:16)

R' Abahu and R' Shimon ben Lakish were once traveling together to Caesarea which lay by the sea. R' Abahu, who had been there before, knew that the people of that city were not good Jews. They had abandoned Torah and *mitzvos* to follow the ways of the gentiles. And his heart pained him when he thought of this.

He turned to R' Shimon ben Lakish and said, "Perhaps we should stay away from such an evil place where the inhabitants curse the Torah and its scholars?"

R' Shimon frowned. He reined in his donkey and dismounted. Then he bent down, took up a handful of sand and shoved it into his friend's mouth!

R' Abahu spit it out, shouting, "What is this? What are you doing?"

"*Hashem*, the G-d of Israel," said R' Shimon, "does not want anyone speaking evil of His children. Even if they sin, they are still His children; He continues to love them! It is our duty, yours and mine, to rebuke them and make them repent, not to speak ill of them!"

R' Abahu felt ashamed. R' Shimon was right.

(Adapted from Shir Hashirim Rabbah 1)

Lashon Hara About Oneself

"לֹא תֵלֵךְ רָכִיל בְּעַמֶּיךָ"

You shall not bear gossip among your people (19:16)

The two men settled back in their seats. They were both on their way to Radin. One of them was the Chafetz Chaim who lived there; the other was a stranger to that city and he was unaware of the identity of his famous fellow passenger.

As travelers will, the two struck up a conversation. The other said to the Chafetz Chaim, "I am going to Radin to see the famous Chafetz Chaim. I want to get a blessing from that famous *tzaddik*. I have come a long way, but it is worth it; he is such a holy man. A blessing from him will surely have influence in heaven."

His companion did not react at all.

He continued, "It must be wonderful living in the same town together with such a great man! You must see him often, hear many stories of his greatness. What a *z'chus!*"

That finally aroused his seatmate, "The Chafetz Chaim is nobody special at all. He is no different from anyone else. Just a simple Jew!"

In anger, the stranger jumped to his feet and cried, "How dare you!"

"But I am telling the truth," said the Chafetz Chaim. "I know the Chafetz Chaim, personally. He is just another Jew."

The stranger grew livid with rage. "What insolence," he said. "How dare you speak against the Chafetz Chaim. I refuse to share a seat with someone like you!" He gathered up his things and stalked out of the train compartment.

The train finally reached Radin. As soon as it stopped, the stranger rushed out. He did not want to meet up again with the Jew who had disparaged the Chafetz Chaim.

He made his way towards the Chafetz Chaim's house. He knocked on the door and was told the master was not at home.

"We expect him any minute, though," they said. "Won't

you come inside and wait, please?"

The visitor was all excited. Soon he would be face to face with the great man. Here he was already, in the Chafetz Chaim's very home! He waited impatiently. He sat down, but almost immediately jumped up. He paced the room, back and forth. Another minute, another minute, and he would be face to face with him.

His heart skipped when he heard the sound of footsteps.

There was a knock at the door and the knob turned. But what was this! Could it be? Was he dreaming? In walked the old man who had sat beside him at the beginning of the train ride! This was his home. He — he was the Chafetz Chaim!

The stranger felt his knees knock together; his tongue stuck to the roof of his mouth, he turned white. He stepped forward with faltering steps and said, "Now I understand... Please, forgive me. I didn't mean to insult you."

"There is no need to apologize," the Chafetz Chaim said. "Actually, I am the one who should apologize, for I see that what I said on the train offended and disturbed you. But, I learned a lesson on the train. I learned something very important: under no circumstances may one speak *lashon hara* — even about oneself!"

Hearty Thanks

"הוֹכֵחַ תּוֹכִיחַ אֶת עֲמִיתֶךָ"
You shall indeed rebuke your comrade (19:17)

R' Hillel Lichenstein of Kolomai used to travel from place to place, exhorting people to do *teshuvah*.

Once, R' Hillel reached Sanz and went to pay his respects to the great R' Chaim Sanzer. In the course of their 'speaking in learning' R' Chaim said, "You give *musar* to the whole world. I, too, would like to have you point out my faults."

R' Hillel looked around the room and said, "I am surprised that you do not have the required *zecher lechurban* (the unpainted square opposite the entrance which is supposed to remind a Jew that the *Beis Hamikdash* is in ruins)."

Without saying a word, R' Chaim went to fetch a ladder. He climbed up. He drew a square and then scratched off the paint within that square. When he had finished he climbed down the ladder, turned to his guest and said, "*Yasher koach!* Hearty thanks!"

He Stole and Was Appeased

"וְלֹא תִשָּׂא עָלָיו חֵטְא"

And you shall not bear a sin against him (19:17)

A poor man once came to R' Nachum of Chernobel, begging for alms. R' Nachum opened the chest where he kept his charity funds and gave the man a sizeable amount. On his way out, the man noticed a silver spoon lying on the table.

"Hmmm. This is also worth money," he thought and quickly slipped it into his pocket.

The maid entered just in time to see the man steal the spoon. She accused him.

The shouting brought R' Nachum to the door. "What is going on here?" he asked.

"He took a spoon," said the maid. "Why wasn't he satisfied with the generous donation that you gave him? Why did he have to take our silver spoon?"

Instead of hanging his head in shame, the beggar shouted, "R' Nachum said I could have the spoon."

Everyone realized that this was an out-and-out lie, but R' Nachum rushed forward to defend the poor man. He could not bear to see a Jew embarrassed.

"I said that he could have the spoon. Leave him alone."

The man could not let well enough alone. "Aha! See! I was right! This spoon is rightfully mine! And I have been unjustly embarrassed. I demand compensation!"

At once R' Nachum took a sum of money, gave it to him and asked forgiveness.

Without a Hint of Resentment

"לֹא תִקֹּם וְלֹא תִטֹּר אֶת־בְּנֵי עַמֶּךָ"

You shall not seek revenge and you shall not bear a grudge against your fellow countryman (19:18)

R' Yisrael Salanter was traveling from Kovna to Vilna. He was dressed simply and traveling by himself. Beside him sat a young man who had obviously spent the past few years being supported by his father-in-law. He was now making his way into the world, looking for a position.

R' Yisrael was smoking a cigarette. This was, after all, the smokers' compartment. The young man turned to him and exclaimed rudely, "Put out that cigarette. I can't stand the smell."

R' Yisrael could easily have told him that it was the smoking compartment. But R' Yisrael did not do so. Without a word, he extinguished the cigarette. A few minutes later the young man raised his voice again, "Close that window! It's freezing here! You can catch pneumonia from such a draft!"

"I am not the one who opened it," R' Yisrael commented, but obliged and shut the window.

The train pulled into Vilna, and a huge crowd of people was on hand awaiting their great leader, R' Yisrael. When the young man got off the train, he saw the throngs and asked why there was such a crowd. What was the occasion?

"Don't you know?" he was told. "R' Yisrael Salanter was on that train. He has just arrived here."

All at once the young man realized that the man with whom he had shared the compartment had been none other than the famous R' Yisrael. He shriveled up with shame.

All that night he relived the scene on the train, cringing at his disgraceful behavior. How had he dared to speak thus to such a man! He could not sleep a wink that night.

When morning arrived, he made his way to R' Yisrael's lodgings; he had to beg forgiveness.

To his surprise, R' Yisrael spoke to him warmly when he entered the room. "Good morning! How are you? Did you have a restful night after yesterday's long journey?" the great man asked kindly.

In the face of such an unexpected welcome he burst into tears. With garbled words he begged forgiveness for his disgraceful behavior.

"You have nothing to be upset about, my dear young man," R' Yisrael comforted him. "I have no hard feelings against you in the least!"

The young man got up to leave, but R' Yisrael detained him with a hand on his sleeve. "Tell me, what has brought you to Vilna?"

The young man said that he wished to become a *shochet*. He had come to Vilna to get his *semichah* accreditation.

"Fine! Then perhaps I can help you. My son-in-law is one of the chief rabbis here."

He led the young man directly to the rabbi who began testing him at once. It did not take long for the rabbi to see that the young man did not know the first thing about the laws of *shechitah!*

With his gentle tone and manner, R' Yisrael turned to him and said, "You must still be tired from the trip. Why don't you go to your hotel and rest up. Come back in a few days and you can take another test."

The young man left. A few days passed but he did not return.

When R' Yisrael realized that he did not intend to be retested, he went to his hotel and sought him out. "Why didn't you come back?" he asked kindly.

"I am grateful to you for having opened my eyes. I realize that I am not fit to become a *shochet.* I intend to return home."

R' Yisrael would not allow that. "You must not say that," he said. "You were not sufficiently prepared, but that does not mean that you are not fit to be a *shochet.* You must review the laws and learn them well. Then, when you are ready, you can take the test again." R' Yisrael did more than advise him. He found an expert *shochet* who was willing to teach the young man. And he prayed for the young man, asking *Hashem* to open up his mind and have him absorb the laws that he needed to know.

R' Yisrael's labors soon bore fruit. The young man studied diligently and seriously, and soon became an expert *shochet.* He received his *semichah* from several prominent rabbis. But still R' Yisrael did not rest; he found him an excellent position.

People would ask R' Yisrael why he had taken such an interest in that young man and involved himself so much in helping him.

He replied, "When the young man came to ask my forgiveness I gave it to him readily. Still, being human, I feared that perhaps I still bore him a grudge in my heart, minute as it might be. I, therefore, had to uproot it by helping him out in every way I could. I did not want to bear even the slightest ill will towards him..."

On One Foot

"וְאָהַבְתָּ לְרֵעֲךָ כָּמוֹךָ"

Love your neighbor like your own self (19:18)

A non-Jew once came to Shammai and said, "I would like to become a Jew but I want to learn everything that there is to know while standing on one foot."

This made Shammai furious. Was this man a fool or did he wish to make a fool of Shammai?! There was so much to learn! How much can a person absorb while standing on one foot?!

"A person can study Torah for his entire life and still not know everything!" Shammai said and grabbing his stick, he chased the gentile away.

The gentile was not discouraged. He went to the gentle Hillel.

"I would like to convert to Judaism," he said, "but on one condition; I want to learn the entire Torah on one foot."

"Very well," Hillel agreed.

The man balanced himself on one foot and waited.

Hillel said: "Whatever is hateful to you, do not do unto others! This is the essence of the entire Torah! But now you must go and learn all of the laws so that you will know how to put this rule into practice."

The gentile agreed. He found himself a teacher, studied Torah, and became a fine Jew.

(Adapted from Tractate Shabbos 31)

The Rebbe Weeps

"וְאָהַבְתָּ לְרֵעֲךָ כָּמוֹךְ"
Love your neighbor like your own self (19:18)

The entire congregation was in a turmoil. Round-the-clock watches were saying *Tehillim;* people were continually knocking at the Rebbe's door to find out the patient's condition. Others were offering their assistance, suggesting doctors from near and far. The Rebbe's son, R' David of Lelov's young son, was in critical condition. When even *Tehillim* did not help, the people of Lelov announced a public fast.

Finally, the Healer of all sick heard their prayers. R' David's young son began recuperating.

When the boy was back on his feet, the entire congregation was invited to a feast of thanksgiving for his recovery. Everyone came, for the Rebbe was most beloved. How surprised people were, though, to find R'

David seated at the head of the table, weeping instead of rejoicing!

"Why are you weeping?" everyone asked. "Is this not an occasion to rejoice?"

"How shall I not weep?" said the Rebbe, tears streaming down his cheeks. "My dear son was seriously ill several weeks ago. Everyone here in Lelov was concerned; everyone prayed for his recovery, even fasted for his sake. No one went to bed at night without offering a special prayer for him. Everyone participated in my distress. And thanks to *Hashem*, your heartfelt prayers were answered. But what happens when someone else, a simple Jew, becomes ill? Does everyone pray for his recovery? Is everyone concerned in the same way? Does anyone say *Tehillim* for him? Shall I not weep for all those forsaken people who are alone in their time of need?"

The Russians Are Coming!

"וְאָהַבְתָּ לְרֵעֲךָ כָּמוֹךְ"

Love your neighbor as your own self (19:18)

At the time of this story the Russians ruled Poland. From time to time, the Poles tried to throw off the Russian yoke. Once, a few thousand Poles succeeded in recapturing several of their cities and ousting the Russian rulers. The soldiers were drunk with victory and as usual, the poor Jews were the first to suffer.

The Poles stormed through the city, using their victory as an excuse to stage a pogrom. They robbed and murdered to their hearts' content. When the rioting had quieted down somewhat, they sought a Jewish scapegoat to accuse as a spy. No one but the best would do — the wealthy, influential Jew, Reb Shimshon.

As soon as the Jews learned of the false accusation, they did everything in their power to save Reb Shimshon, but the Poles turned a deaf ear. There was nothing that the Jews could do for their brother.

The day of the execution arrived. Disspiritedly, they gathered together in the *beis medrash*. Suddenly, Reb Nachum, the young *melamed*, burst in, extremely upset. "How can you just sit there when a fellow Jew is going to the gallows this morning?" he shouted. "Why are you all silent? Don't you realize that it is Reb Shimshon whom they are going to hang? Reb Shimshon, who has always had a ready ear and an open hand for others in distress? We cannot let this terrible thing happen! We must do something!"

"Yes! Something must be done before it is too late. But what can we do against hundreds of armed Polish soldiers?" asked one man. "We have requested, pleaded, cried out and offered bribes, but the Poles only want Jewish blood. Not even money will spare Reb Shimshon now.

R' Nachum refused to listen. He rushed from the *beis medrash* like a hurricane and ran straight for the gallows where the executioners were already placing the noose around Reb Shimshon's neck.

Onto the platform he climbed, shouting, "Stop! Wait! You are making a terrible mistake! Reb Shimshon is no spy; he is innocent! How can you hang an innocent man? I'm the spy! I'm the guilty one. I passed on secrets to the Russians. Hang me!"

The Poles, who knew that their case was a trumped one, laughed in Reb Nachum's face. They did not want the blood of some young nobody. They wanted to kill the pride of the Jewish community, Reb Shimshon, not some hysterical madman. They pushed him off the platform.

Reb Nachum was overwrought. He ran around to the other side of the platform, elbowed his way up the stairs and reached the gallows. Despite the blows that rained on his head and shoulders from all sides, he tore the rope from Reb Shimshon's neck.

Suddenly, there was a cry. "The Russians are coming! The Russians are coming!"

The Poles gathered in the city square stampeded, running for their lives. The Russians were coming!

The city square was vacant. Only two people remained, **Reb Shimshon, white as chalk, unable to believe that he was still alive, and Reb Nachum the** *melamed*. **Slowly, in a daze, they walked off the platform together and went to** the *beis medrash* to thank *Hashem* for His miraculous rescue.

But She Is a Widow

"וְאַלְמָנָה הוֹנוּ בָךְ"

They have wronged the widow
(Haftorah Parashas Kedoshim, Yechezkel 22:7)

A group of rabbis and community leaders had gathered in the home of the rabbi of Vilna, R' Chaim Ozer Grodzenski, to discuss many important problems which hovered over the Jewish people.

In the midst of this crucial meeting the door of R' Chaim Ozer's study suddenly flew open. A middle-aged woman barged in and began pounding on the heavy oak table with both of her fists. The rabbis were too dumbfounded to even react.

R' Grodzenski knew this woman, however. She was a member of his community, a trouble-laden woman. He looked upon her with kindly eyes, waiting to hear what she demanded.

"Rabbi!" she screamed hysterically. "I will not leave this room until you write a letter to the *tzedakah* treasurers of the community for me. I demand the proper sum of money to help me out in my business. I will break every chair in this room if I do not get that letter."

R' Chaim Ozer tried to clam her. He opened his own purse and tried to give her a number of coins while explaining the matter. "I am afraid that our charity funds are already earmarked for other causes." But, she refused to listen. Instead, she covered her ears with her hands and continued shouting, threatening violence.

One of the rabbis could no longer bear this disgrace. He raised his own voice so that he might be heard over her shouts.

Suddenly, there was a deafening roar in the room. *"Zol zein shtill!* Silence!"* shouted the usually soft-spoken rabbi of Vilna.

"Leave her be," he said in a pained voice. "She is a widow."

פָּרָשַׁת אֱמֹר

Parashas Emor

The End Does Not Justify
the Means

"וְלֹא תְחַלְלוּ אֶת שֵׁם קָדְשִׁי וְנִקְדַּשְׁתִּי"

*And you shall not desecrate My holy Name and I shall be
sanctified (22:32)*

A well-meaning Cracow Jew once registered his
thirteen-year-old son in a gentile 'gymnasium' (high
school) famed for its high scholastic standards. Since
classes were held on *Shabbos* and Jewish holidays, he
asked for special permission exempting his son from
writing on those days. The principal agreed and the child
was duly enrolled.

When R' Akiva Kornitzer, rabbi of Cracow, learned of
this, he summoned the father who was a frequent visitor
to his home. They had a long talk and the rabbi rebuked
him.

The father, after listening to the rabbi, explained, "But
rabbi, you do not understand. My motives are not selfish.
I have the welfare of our people in mind. In future years
we will need men who are well educated, who can read
and write foreign languages, who are well versed in the
sciences and arts. We need people who can argue against
them on common ground people to represent Jewry

against future anti-Semites. When my son acquires a well rounded education, he will be able to defend our Torah and our people from future prosecutors and persecutors. This will be a true *kiddush Hashem*; he will sanctify *Hashem*'s Name on earth! Don't you see how important that is?" The man expected the rabbi to praise his foresight.

However, instead R' Akiva, perturbed, replied excitedly, "It is this very kind of rationalization against which the Torah warns us! In the *parashah* of *Emor*, it says: 'And you shall not desecrate My holy Name and I shall be sanctified in the midst of *Bnei Yisrael*.' These very words warn us against violating *Hashem*'s holy Name with the purpose of eventually sanctifying it. In other words, the end does not justify the means. Even if your intentions are desirable and praiseworthy, they cannot purify the means which are *treife*, undesirable and dangerous.

The Birth of a City

"וְנִקְדַּשְׁתִּי בְּתוֹךְ בְּנֵי יִשְׂרָאֵל"

And I shall be sanctified in the midst of the Children of Israel
(22:32)

Sacrifice your life and sanctify My Name
(Rashi)

Berditchov is familiar to most people because of the famous R' Levi Yitzchak, 'Defender of Israel'. However, it also has other claims to fame, for it had such leaders as R' Lieber and R' Yosef Charif, to name only two. This home of great scholars and exceptional *tzaddikim* became known as the 'Jerusalem of Vollein', the district in Poland in which it lay. And not only was the city famous to Jews, but even gentiles held it in great esteem, referring to it as the 'Jewish kingdom'.

"Tell me, Rebbe," a chasid once asked of the Admor of Vorki, "why was the city of Berditchov chosen to receive such great rabbis?"

The Rebbe replied, "It is not in vain that this city gained such distinction and can claim exceptional people such as R' Levi Yitzchak. You see, it was founded upon the blood and pain and sighs of a very precious Jew! I see that you are surprised, that you do not know the history of Berditchov. That city was founded upon the suffering of a great man. Its ground soaked up his blood... blood that was spilt by bloodthirsty gentiles. This is how it all began:

Upon the site where Berditchov stands there once stood a thick forest teeming with deer and small game, a wonderland for the hunting which the nobles loved.

The forerunner of the future city was a small village, Bistrich, which had an all-Jewish population. One of this village's most illustrious families was that of R' Avraham Ashkenazi who had fled from pogroms in his native city of Cracow. He was immediately accepted into the heart of the village, for R' Avraham was a wealthy man, established in business, a man of kindness and charity and, above all, a true Torah scholar. He could trace his lineage to such famous people as R' Shimon Ostropoler; R' Natan Shapira, author of "*Megaleh Amukos*' and R' Yechiel Michel of Nemirov — the rabbi who died bravely sanctifying *Hashem*'s Name, during the infamous revolt led by Chemielnicki's murderous hordes of the years that have gone down in history as "Tach veTat'. R' Avraham could even trace his line all the way back to King David. His family had, therefore, always avoided mixing their royal line with the line of priests and had never intermarried with *kohanim*.

R' Avraham had escaped with his life and his family and settled down in Bistrich. Here he built a spacious home on the bank of the river. Close by, on the hill, stood the castle of the Polish nobleman, Count Poskowitz, who owned the very land upon which the village stood.

The terrible ordeal which R' Avraham had just been through took its toll. He did not enjoy serenity for long; shortly after arriving, he left this world for a better one.

R' Avraham left behind a son, R' Lieber, who had no interest in business; he preferred to devote his life to the study of Torah, to uncovering the secrets of the Torah in all of its forms, revealed and mystic. He was a pure, saintly man, who had renounced business and worldly matters.

R' Lieber would begin his day by immersing in the nearby river. He would then row over to the thick forest where he remained to pray and study in total isolation. Here, no one disturbed his concentration. Towards evening he would row back to his home and conduct his charity affairs. R' Lieber had built a special wing for travelers; whoever came to him was assured of a warm meal, a comfortable and clean bed and, when he left, a bag containing plenty of provisions for the journey ahead and, if the man was poor, some coins and clothing. No one was ever turned away!

People referred to him as the 'Big R' Lieber', not only

because of his broad shoulders and towering stature, but because of his great knowledge and his big heart and generous spirit.

His daily routine never varied. The day of our story dawned like any other. R' Lieber made his morning ablutions in the river after which he rowed over to the opposite shore. Enveloping himself in his *tallis* and donning his *tefillin*, R' Lieber began praying to his Maker. Another day of worship and quiet study had begun.

Suddenly, the stillness of the dense forest was broken. A panting deer ran by, fleeing for its life. Short on its heels came the hounds, baying and snarling, hot on the scent. The horses crashed through the underbrush, tossing their heads and neighing in nervous excitement. Their riders, sounding their horns, urging their dogs and horses on, closed in for the kill.

R' Lieber prayed on, oblivious to it all.

It was a hot summer's day. The young count had invited his friends to spend it in the cool of the forest — in the heat of a hunt, his favorite sport. He rushed forward, wanting to strike the fatal blow when, suddenly, a horse reared up, throwing its rider to the ground. The man lay there in a crumpled heap, moaning and groaning for help. The count tore his attention away from the trail of the deer and rushed to the fallen man, his guest. Meanwhile a group had gathered and was trying to administer emergency care by splashing water over the wounded man. The count was puzzled.

"What made the horse shy like that? What made him rear up and throw an experienced rider?" he wondered. Suddenly, he spied a white figure standing upright by a tree. Coming closer, he discovered that it was a Jew, wrapped up in his prayer shawl.

The count, frustrated at having to stop the hunt at the critical moment, raised the whip in his hand to strike at the still figure. He was the culprit; he had frightened the horse into throwing its rider; it was all the Jew's fault! He had wounded his guest; he had ruined the hunt!

Crack! Down went the lash, snapping through the air and onto the Jew's back. Suddenly, there was a wide red stripe across the white *tallis*. Young Count Poskowitz went beserk. His arm went up and down, lashing at the broad back. The *tallis* was no longer white but red.

The sight of blood did not deter the count. He continued to rain blows on the defenseless back.

His friends bore no special love for Jews, but they could not help rushing forward to restrain their half-crazed host. "You will kill him, if you do not stop!" they warned. "You do not want Jewish blood on your hands. There might be a police investigation which would be most unpleasant. Come — let us flee."

At that moment, R' Lieber crumpled to the ground, wallowing in his own blood. This brought the young count somewhat back to his senses and he fled, together with his companions.

Hours passed. The sun had long passed its zenith and was about to hide behind the mountains when R' Lieber finally returned to consciousness. Night shadows were falling. He did not know where he was at first. Just opening his eyes was a supreme effort. Pain shot through every inch of him. With superhuman effort, he crawled to his rowboat. Somehow, he managed to climb in, row across, and reach his home. And he fell away in a faint on his doorstep.

The hunting party continued with their hunt, heading in a different direction. After a pleasant day, they were returning home — to the count's castle — with excellent game caught by their own hands. Everything had gone well and now they were tired, ready for a feast of roast venison at the count's table.

The young count had just stepped into the hall when he turned pale. "What is the matter?" his guests asked in alarm.

"I don't feel well," he said. "I will lie down; I'll join you later when I feel somewhat better."

A servant helped the young master to his bed, but as soon as he sank upon the fresh sheets, the count became partially paralyzed. His right hand refused to move; his right foot would not obey his command.

His father, the old count, was terrified. "Bring a doctor! Quick!" he shouted. Before long the count's private physician was examining the patient. He could find no cause for the paralysis. It puzzled him.

"Why don't you call in another doctor for consultation? I can make no sense out of this illness," the doctor himself suggested. Others were called, but none of them understood the nature of his sudden paralysis. By now the father was frantic, for the malady was spreading to all parts of his son's body. It crept up until it reached his mouth, twisting it into a strange shape.

"Get the royal physican, the king's own private doctor," the old count begged. But when he came, he could not diagnose the young count's illness.

"I don't know what is wrong, but your son is very ill. He may not have long to live. Only prayer can help him now," the royal physician said, throwing his hands up helplessly. "Go assemble all of your tenants, all the Christians on your land. Have them say mass and light candles for your son. And see to it that the Jews, also, pray for him."

"But there isn't even one synagogue in the entire area," one of the servants commented.

"What? No synagogue?" the old count asked in surprise. "Where do they pray, then? Jews are always praying, aren't they?"

"They pray in the home of a certain R' Lieber, who is considered a very saintly Jew, a holy person. But, as of the moment, he is bedridden."

"Why? What is the matter with him?"

The servant became confused and muttered, half under his breath, "I heard that he was beaten badly with a whip. He is very sick..."

"Who flogged him?" asked the count.

The servant turned red and began stammering, "The y-y-young count, Sir."

"What?!" he said in astonishment. "My son, the young count?!"

The old man began trembling. All at once, he realized why the young count was so ill — and why the best doctors were unable to cure him. This was his punishment from on High for having harmed a holy man.

The count rushed out of the house and down the hill to the home of R' Lieber. He found the Jew writhing upon his bed, unable to find any comfortable position. His back was one flaming, raw welt. But when the rabbi saw the count, he tried to raise himself on one arm and bow his head in greeting.

The old man fell at his bedside, begging, "Please pray for my son. He has been punished for having dared to touch you. He is now lying in bed, paralyzed from head to foot. He will not have long to live unless you forgive him and pray for his recovery. Please, he is only a foolish youth who did not know better."

"I will pray for him, but only on one condition," said R' Lieber.

"Anything. Whatever you say, rabbi. Only let my son get better. Don't let my only son die!"

"You must build a synagogue for the Jewish community right on the spot where my blood was shed. On the earth which soaked up my blood, you must also build a *mikveh* and dwellings for the overflow population of Bistrich. This site must become a city, a center for Judaism, a living memorial to the innocent Jewish blood shed so cruelly."

"Whatever you say, Rabbi. But please pray for my son."

The old count returned home and launched into the construction at once. A surveyor marked the lines of a new city; architects drew up plans and before long a magnificent dome shaped building stood proudly where there had once been forest. Houses were built and, slowly, a new city took shape.

R' Lieber recovered slowly. When he was able to leave his bed, he went to visit the young count whose condition had remained the same. He still lay paralyzed from head to foot. R' Lieber told him to move his right hand and with an intense effort and concentration, the young count was suddenly able to move that limb.

R' Lieber visited him time after time, restoring a different part of the count's body to normal function with each visit. The old count was overjoyed at the progress.

The day on which he was finally able to leave his bed and stand on his own two feet was one of general rejoicing — because that was the day that the *beis knesses* was dedicated.

After that, the construction and settlement of the new city progressed rapidly.

The new city flourished, drawing many new residents. It throbbed with Jewish life. At first it was called Berditchovka but when Count Radziwil purchased that entire region, he shortened its name to Berditchov.

From a small town it grew into a big city, attracting both Jews and non-Jews. Berditchov's first rabbi was R' Lieber, its founder, who was blessed with long years. R' R' Lieber, a devoted follower of the Baal Shem Tov, was specially honored with many private audiences with him. When R' Lieber was one hundred years old he passed away.

His successor was R' Levi Yitzchak. At first people resented him, feeling that no one could be worthy of following in R' Lieber's footsteps. But, when R' Levi Yitzchak released the waters from the *mikveh* — the spring which R' Lieber had used — and which had become clogged upon his death — they saw this as a heavenly sign of his worth. Then he became accepted by all.

The *Admor* of Vorka had ended his tale; the chasid, now, understood.

The very ground upon which Berdichov was founded had soaked up the blood of a holy man. No wonder, then, that it had deserved the great R' Levi Yitzchak, the leader who became the "Defender of Israel', not only for Berditchov, or for his generation, but for many generations to come."

R' Yonasan's Tree

"מִשְׁפָּט אֶחָד יִהְיֶה לָכֶם"

There shall be one law for you (24:22)

R' Yonasan the *dayan* lived in a house surrounded by a yard. At the edge of this yard, right by the gate, towered a huge tree whose branches hung over into his neighbor's yard. This neighbor, a Roman, and R' Yonasan enjoyed good relations. The Roman never complained that the tree annoyed him, that it shed leaves in his yard, or that the shade kept the sun out.

Once, two men came to be judged before R' Yonasan. It was a summer day and the window was wide open, so that his neighbor, the Roman, could not help overhearing the case.

"We are neighbors," began one of the men. "We share a common fence between our properties. But this man has a huge tree growing in his yard whose branches overhang into mine. This disturbs me very much. My wife cannot hang out her laundry there, since the tree hides the sun. She cannot put our child out to play in the sun either. All in all, it is a big nuisance. I demand that he cut down the overhanging branches."

R' Yonasan listened to him and said, "Come back tomorrow and I will give you my decision."

R' Yonasan's neighbor was very curious to know what that decision would be, since R' Yonasan also had such a tree, the branches of which hung over into his yard.

The next day, the two men returned. The Roman neighbor crept up under R' Yonasan's window, so as not to miss a word of the exchange. The judge began, "I will review the case first just to clarify the issue. You, Reuven, have a large tree the branches of which hang over onto Shimon's property. You, Shimon, demand that he cut off those branches since they disturb you for various reasons. Very well, the *halachah* is explicit in such a case. Reuven, you must saw off the branches which cast a shade onto Shimon's property. It is that simple."

When the Roman heard this, he burst into the room. "And what about you, rabbi? Why don't you practice what you yourself preach? Why don't you cut off the branches of your own tree before telling others to cut off theirs?"

R' Yonasan put a hand on his sleeve and said, "Let us all go out to the yard for a moment." The three men filed out behind R' Yonasan to see what he had to show them. And there was his towering tree, no longer symmetrical with arms outstretched to all sides. It stood straight but looked lopsided, with half of its branches sawn off. "That is what you must do, Reuven," said R' Yonasan. "Shimon need not suffer from your tree."

He then turned to the Roman, "Even though you had never complained about the tree, I did not want to judge this case until I had done what our Torah requires. Only then did I feel qualified to tell others what to do."

The Roman was deeply impressed and said, "Blessed be the G-d of the Jews Who gave them laws and judges as righteous and just as these!"

(Adapted from Talmud Yerushalmi, Bava Basra, Chapter 2:11)

The Gooseherd's Songs

"וְאֶת עַמִּי יוֹרוּ בֵּין קֹדֶשׁ לְחֹל"

*And they shall guide My people in what is sacred and what is
not sacred
(Haftorah Parashas Emor, Yechezkel 44:23)*

The saintly R' Leib Sarah's was visiting one *Shabbos* in
Russia when, suddenly, he had a holy vision. He was
wide awake, but his eyes looked far beyond the room. He
could see all the way to Hungary, to a village called
Sirintash. An exalted soul, which needed his help to reach
its true heights, was to be found there.

That night, after *havdalah*, R' Leib ordered his wagoner
to hitch up the horses. They were going on a 'long trip'.

The wagoner knew exactly what this meant. They
would indeed be going far, covering miles with each lift
of the horses' feet. The road would flow beneath the
wheels of the wagon, as they made a miraculous distance-
leap, a *kefitzas haderech*, to reach their destination.

And so it was. Up they mounted and as soon as they
reached the outskirts of the village R' Leib took the reins
from him and drove. The wagoner fell into a dream-like
trance. Fast asleep, he saw the trees and houses flash by,
village and town skim across his vision. The horses never
faltered at a crossroads. They never felt the tug of the
reins to the right or the left but cantered straight ahead,
sure of their destination. Up mountains, down valleys,
through thick forests or bare wastelands, their hooves
beat a steady tattoo, never tiring.

And then, just as they approached their destination,

they slowed down to a steady trot. The wagoner awoke, took the reins in hand and waited for R' Leib to tell him where to stop.

After a long night's drive, they entered the village of Sirintash, early Sunday morning, and stopped by the synagogue. After prayer, R' Leib entered a nearby forest to meditate. Peace and quiet reigned. Suddenly, the silence was broken by the honking of geese. Soon an eight-year-old boy came into sight, followed by a flock of geese. R' Leib stood up. The boy approached. He was dressed in patches and tatters; his cheeks were sunken, his face pale. Bony arms protruded from his worn sleeves and he shuffled along in shoes, sizes too big. But his eyes! His eyes had an unearthly light shining in them, reflecting a sublime spirit within, casting a glow upon his thin face. This was the soul which R' Leib must redeem and offer to the world, so that all of Jewry could bask in its holy light. R' Leib drew nearer and spoke softly so as not to alarm him.

R' Leib said in a fatherly voice. "Tell me, what is your name? Where do you live?"

"My name is Yitzchak Isaac," he replied in a firm, clear voice. "I live with my widowed mother in a small cottage at the end of the forest."

R' Leib went to the widow and said, "You have a very special son. He is destined to brighten the eyes of Jewry with his Torah and lighten the burden of the *galus* with his deep, soulful songs. You must entrust your son to the right person, a *tzaddik* who will develop all of his hidden talents and draw out his holy soul. As for the few pennies which he earns by herding geese, I will give you enough money to support you till the end of your days."

The widow sighed and wiped a few tears from her

eyes. Her mother's heart had long since told her that her son was special. She could not be selfish and keep this gift for herself. She must let *klal Yisrael* benefit. Choked with emotion, she could not reply, only nod.

R' Leib waited until the boy returned. Leaving a large sum of money on the table for the widow, he took the boy by the hand and led him to his wagon.

The wagon made its rapid way from Sirintash in Hungary to Nikolsburg, where the holy R' Shmelke served as rabbi.

Leading the small boy by the hand, R' Leib entered R' Shmelke's *beis medrash* and said, "This is a special boy whose soul has come to this world directly from the heavenly spheres of music and song. He is destined to contribute much to our people. But he is delicate; he must be nurtured and cared for. He must be brought up in the home of a great *tzaddik* who will develop his greatness. R' Shmelke, I entrust him into your great hands."

The little gooseherd remained in R' Shmelke's home and grew up there. The years in the forest were not totally forgotten; he remembered the songs he had sung to his geese. He retained the lovely, simple melodies but changed the words, transforming these songs to holy prayers expressing the love of the Jewish people for their Heavenly Father, their pain and suffering in the Exile, their deep longing for the coming of the *Mashiach*.

He had once sung the simple words:

Oh forest, oh forest, how vast you are,
Oh flower, oh flower, how far away.
Were you not so vast,
How much closer the flower would be.
If only I could leave you,

Then I and the flower could be together...

He set these words to the melody:

Galus, galus, how long are you,

Shechinah, Shechinah, how far away.

Were the *galus* not so long,

How much closer the *Shechinah* would be.

Take us out of the *galus*,

We two will be together...

R' Leib had found the perfect place for this precious soul. Here, in R' Shmelke's house, the gooseherd was transformed to a leader of Jewry. He became the famous R' Yitzchak Isaac Taub of Kaliv, whose soulful song-prayers earned him the title 'Sweet Singer of Israel', like King David.

When the *tzaddik* R' Naftali of Ropshitz once heard R' Yitzchak Isaac sing his famous song about the Exile and the *Shechinah*, he burst out, "When the Kaliver Rebbe sings that song, he causes a great upheaval in heaven. He unleashes the wellsprings of heavenly mercy. Then hosts upon hosts of angels go forth to greet the *tzaddik* R' Leib Sarah's in his palace in heaven. And they praise him, saying, 'Blessed are you for having bequeathed this precious soul to mankind.'"

פָּרָשַׁת בְּהַר

Parashas Behar

Bee Honey and Fig Honey

"אַל תּוֹנוּ אִישׁ אֶת אָחִיו"

Do not deceive one another (25:14)

This refers to deception in money matters

(Rashi)

R' Chanaya was a great Sage who lived in Tzipori in *Eretz Yisrael*. While he devoted most of his time to Torah study, he would not accept any money for it, but supported his family from the sale of honey. His warehouse held many barrels of both bee and fig honey.

Once a group of merchants arrived in town. They had come from a different city and wished to purchase a large quantity of honey. They went to R' Chanina's warehouse, bought their many barrels of honey and paid a large sum in cash. Their business completed, they loaded the barrels upon their camels and donkeys and set out homeward, very satisfied.

R' Chananya rearranged the barrels in the warehouse, moving some here, others there to make room for the next batch of honey. When R' Chananya was about to lock up his warehouse and return to the *beis midrash*, he, suddenly, realized that he had mistakenly not sold his last customers bee honey, as he had thought, but fig honey!

He rushed out to the street, hoping to catch the men and correct his mistake before it was too late. Perhaps, they had stopped somewhere, for a drink...

He looked right and left; he asked the people in the marketplace if they had seen the caravan of merchants, but was told that they had already gone, some time ago. R' Chananya went to his *beis midrash*, hoping that the men would return themselves, when they realized the mistake.

His error troubled him; it lay on his conscience for days and days. He had cheated people by not selling them what they had asked for. How he longed to set things straight!

Time passed and those same merchants returned to Tzipori to buy a fresh stock of honey. R' Chananya recognized them immediately. He rushed up to them and apologized profusely. "I am so sorry! I made a terrible mistake last time you were here. Instead of bee honey, I gave you fig honey. You must forgive me! I cheated you, I deceived you! Please, now that you are here, you must come to my warehouse and let me repair the damage. I will give you the same amount of honey, bee honey this time, for free!"

"No," they said to R' Chananya. "You have no reason to feel sorry. On the contrary, the fig honey which you gave us was even better for the purpose we needed. We were very satisfied with it and want more of the same. How much can you sell us this time?"

R' Chananya sighed with relief. He had not cheated anyone, after all! How relieved he was! That matter had been disturbing him all this time. He did not want to charge them, but they refused.

R' Chananya was left, holding the money. He did not

feel good about accepting this money even though there was no question about it rightfully belonging to him. He had certainly given the people their money's worth. Last time and this time. In fact, they had been especially pleased!

Yet, he went beyond the letter of the law and set aside that entire sum, a large one, for public welfare; he donated it for the building of a new *beis midrash* in Tzipori!

Two Cents Worth

"אַל תּוֹנוּ אִישׁ אֶת אָחִיו"

Do not deceive one another (25:14)

This refers to deception in money matters

(Rashi)

R' Avraham Galanti, a great sage who was a fellow townsman of the Arizal, once came to him with a request.

"Rabbenu," he said, very humbly, "I am very troubled. My soul is not at rest. I feel that there is some sin which I have committed, but it eludes me. I would like to do *teshuvah*, but I cannot, since I do not know where my fault lies. I know that you are a holy man who can read souls. Tell me, by looking at my forehead — what have I done wrong? Give me a *tikun*, a way of mending what I have damaged."

The Ari was taken aback. R' Avraham was a very holy man himself. How could he have sinned? And who was he, the Ari, to tell R' Avraham what to do?!

With tears in his eyes, R' Avraham begged him just to look at his forehead and see if he saw anything written there.

The Ari studied R' Avraham's face, looked intently at his forehead, then said with a sigh, "I do see a trace of something. Your sin has something to do with stealing."

R' Avraham was horrified! "What have I become," he cried, "to be guilty of theft!"

R' Avraham went home feeling worse than ever. Now, he was certain that he had sinned, but he did not know *how* he had stolen.

R' Avraham owned a textile mill. He employed people who worked his looms and produced fine fabrics which he sold. Could he have cheated his customers? He did not think so. He let them determine the worth of his merchandise and would accept what they paid him. It must be that he had cheated his workers.

When R' Avraham reached home, he ripped his clothing and put on sackcloth and ashes, as if he were in mourning. Then, he went to his factory and called the workers to attention. They were horrified to see R' Avraham thus, for they loved him dearly.

"What is the matter, R' Avraham?" they said as they swarmed around him. "Why are you in mourning?"

R' Avraham replied, "I am only flesh and blood; human. When I die, I do not want to go to *gehinnom* for having stolen or cheated anyone. As long as I am still alive, I wish to right any wrongs I have done to you, each and every one of you. If I have not paid any of you what is due, I wish to make amends."

He opened a purse full of coins and emptied it out on a large table. "Take! Take! Anyone who feels that I owe him anything should take."

No one moved. No one lifted a finger to the pile of glittering coins on the table. After a few moments, his workers said, "R' Avraham, did we ever complain about being mistreated? On the contrary, you are the best employer that anyone could possibly wish for! You give us a monthly salary, without ever checking if we worked the full time or not. You have always been more than fair; you are very generous and so, we never bothered to reckon up each minute of work, even if we stayed late to finish up an urgent order. We are very happy to work for you and never felt that we deserved more than we got. You never told us to measure our exact production by what you paid us and so we never did, being happy to work and take the money you gave us. But why do you, suddenly, suspect that you cheated us? And even if you did, we forgive you wholeheartedly!"

R' Avraham looked around at his staff of workers. How loyal they all were! How devoted! And how honest! But perhaps he had cheated someone after all. He tried again,

"Think carefully. Think back. Perhaps I did not pay someone his full due? The money is yours. Feel free to take whatever you think you deserve."

Not a soul moved. Finally, however, after a long pause, one woman drew near the table and took two pennies. Then she went back to her place. R' Avraham waited, but no one else stepped forward. He decided to return to the Ari. He wanted to know if there was anything else he should do.

R' Avraham Galanti went back to the Ari and begged

him to look at his forehead again. The Ari looked carefully, then shook his head.

"There is nothing there now. Your sin has been erased. Do you know what your sin was? I will tell you now. There is a woman on your staff who is an expert weaver. She works faster and better than the rest and thus, really deserves a little more money, though she never took any. Now, that you insisted, she took two pennies more than the others. In heaven, they took you to task for not recognizing her superior talent and paying her for it. Now that you have, your 'sin' is canceled and the mark, the stigma, is erased from your forehead!"

First Things First

"אַל תּוֹנוּ אִישׁ אֶת אָחִיו"
Do not deceive one another (25:14)

This refers to deception in money matters

(Rashi)

R' Yisrael Salant, father of the *musar* movement, taught people how important it was to be honest and to do one's duty towards one's fellow man.

Once a new *chazzan* was appointed to the *shul* where R' Yisrael prayed. The *chazzan*, who was conscientious, came to R' Yisrael and asked, "What holy thoughts must I bear in mind while I am standing before the congregation and leading it in prayer?"

R' Yisrael replied, "The first thing that you must do is to learn the proper *niggunim* (melodies) for all of the prayers! You must be able to sing the prayers well."

The *chazzan* had not expected such an answer. He looked surprised. He had not asked about melodies, he had asked about inner sublime thoughts — *kavanos*!

"Yes, indeed!" R' Yisrael nodded. "The most important thing, as far as your job is concerned, is that you know how to sing the correct tunes to the prayers, that you lead the *davening* as is expected of you. If you are not a good *chazzan*, if you do not sing well, then you are defrauding your congregation and not doing the job for which you were hired. First and foremost, you are being paid to sing well. That is your primary obligation. For if you do not do so, are you not cheating your employers?"

Not like a Cedar

"וְלֹא תוֹנוּ אִישׁ אֶת עֲמִיתוֹ"

You shall not deceive your fellow Jew (25:17)
The Torah warns against deceiving with words — a
person should not tease (distress) his fellow Jew

(Rashi)

Shimon ben Elazar had left his town as a youth. His father had sent him to a *yeshivah* to study Torah and now, many years later, he was returning home. How proud he felt.

"Everyone," he thought, "remembers me as the little boy who ran barefoot through the village streets, who climbed apple trees and swam in the river. Now I am coming back with the title 'Rabbi'. How proud my parents will be. How proud my childhood teachers and all the people who knew me will be. They will surely be waiting to welcome me, the great sage! This is a happy day for me."

Feeling very smug and self-satisfied, R' Shimon hardly noticed his donkey step aside to make way for a fellow traveler on foot. The man looked up and saw R' Shimon. He could tell by just looking at him that this man was a *talmid chacham* and bowed low.

"Shalom to you, Rabbi!" he said respectfully.

R' Shimon was shaken from his pleasant daydreams and looked down at the man on the road. His face was pockmarked and his head misshapen and he was also hunchbacked. R' Shimon recoiled from him, saying, without even thinking, "How ugly you are! Are all the people where you come from as ugly as you?"

The man winced. He knew he was not a pleasant sight to look at, but it hurt to be reminded of his ugliness. Surely, a scholar should have known better than to insult him like that! "I don't know. But if my appearance does not please you, why don't you go to the craftsman who made me? Tell him that he made an inferior product."

R' Shimon suddenly realized what he had done. He understood what the man was saying: if he, R' Shimon, found him ugly, he should go to *Hashem*, the Creator, and complain...

R' Shimon felt terrible. He had insulted a human being. It wasn't the stranger's fault that he was ugly. But it *was* R' Shimon's sin to have insulted him!

Jumping off his donkey, he fell at the man's feet and wept, "Please forgive me! I spoke hastily, not realizing what I was saying! I did not really mean to hurt you! I am sorry!"

"No, I will not forgive you! Why should I? You should not have said such a thing, nor even thought such a thing. If you want me to forgive you, first go to the One Who created me and complain to Him." The man turned his back on R' Shimon and continued on his way.

R' Shimon did not remount his donkey. With head bowed in shame, he walked behind the ugly man and kept on begging that he forgive him. The man ignored him.

Thus they walked, R' Shimon begging forgiveness, the ugly man refusing to forgive him.

Finally, they reached the outskirts of R' Shimon's town. Just as he had expected, there was the entire population, turned out to greet the returning scholar. As soon as they saw him, they rushed forward to greet him.

"*Shalom aleichem, morenu verabenu!*" they exclaimed. "Welcome home, master and scholar!"

The ugly man turned to them with a sneer. "Is that the man whom you call your master and teacher? If *he* is a teacher, let there be few like him amongst our people!"

The people were stunned. What did he mean? "Why do you say so?" they asked, horrified.

The man told them what had happened.

"But even if he has insulted you, you must forgive him. See how sorry he is, how he regrets having spoken without thinking. After all, he is a great scholar and you must respect the knowledge of the Torah which he has acquired," the townspeople begged.

Finally, the ugly man agreed to forgive R' Shimon. "But

only on condition that he never repeats such a thing again! In the future, he should think before he speaks."

How relieved R' Shimon was to hear this. He had learned a very important lesson just now and he wished to teach it to others. Before even going home, he went straight to the *beis midrash* and gathered all the scholars around him and said, "A person should always be soft and pliable like a reed and not proud and unbending like a cedar."

A person should be kind and pleasant to others and not boastful and haughty or unyielding like the tall cedar which bruises anyone who comes up against it!

(Adapted from Tractate Taanis 20)

Enough Room For Everyone

"וְלֹא תוֹנוּ אִישׁ אֶת עֲמִיתוֹ"
You shall not deceive one another (25:17)

R' Pinchas Menachem Yustman of Piltz used to tell the following story about the Gerrer Rebbe, the *Chidushei Harim*:

When the *Chidushei Harim* once overheard a Jew calling someone else by his nickname, Reuven *der schvartzer* — Reuven the dark one, he got very angry and said to his *chasidim*, "By using that nickname people lose their portion in *olam haba* — the World-to-Come!"

And upon another occasion, he heard someone calling to another, "Hey, you, Blind Yossi! Come here. I have something important to tell you!"

The Gerrer Rebbe shuddered and said, "Who gave you permission to insult such an unfortunate person?"

The man tried to justify himself, "But everyone calls him that!"

"Hardly an answer. There is plenty of room in *gehinnom* for all of them!"

Not to Embarrass A Jew

"וְלֹא תוֹנוּ אִישׁ אֶת עֲמִיתוֹ"
You shall not deceive one another (25:17)

"I have made a vow which I would like to absolve," said the man who had come to the Chazon Ish, R' Avraham Yeshaya Karelitz. "I am unable to keep it and would like a *hataras nedarim*."

Three learned people are required to make a *beis din* to dissolve oaths. Since there was a *talmid chacham* already in the room besides the Chazon Ish, the latter told the man to step outside and fetch a third man.

The man went outside and without thinking, chose a man off the Bnei Brak street. It just so happened, that the third man was not a learned man but a simple Jew.

The Chazon Ish questioned the man who had made the

vow. Since the man had not realized all the consequences of his vow, there was a *halachic* 'opening', grounds, to annul it. With the help of the two other members of the *beis din*, the Chazon Ish was able to cancel the vow.

Having done his duty, the simple Jew left the room and returned to his affairs. As soon as the door closed behind him, the Chazon Ish turned to the others and said, "Actually, the vow is not yet canceled. The *hataras neder* was not valid. You see, that Jew was not really qualified to serve on this *beis din*, since he has no *halachic* knowledge of this matter. We must try all over again. But I went through the entire process, because I did not want to insult him; I only pretended to annul the vow."

That is Not the Answer

"וְנָתְנָה הָאָרֶץ פִּרְיָהּ וַאֲכַלְתֶּם לָשׂבַע... וְכִי תֹאמְרוּ מַה נֹּאכַל
בַּשָּׁנָה הַשְּׁבִיעִית... וְצִוִּיתִי אֶת בִּרְכָתִי"

And the land will give its fruit and you shall eat to satiety... And
if you ask: what shall we eat in the seventh year... I shall
command My blessing (25, 19-21)

A ll his life he had dreamed about *Eretz Yisrael*, the land of his ancestors, the Promised Land. And when he finally was able to realize his dream and settle in the holy city of Tzefas, in the Galilee, R' Avraham Tzvi of Avritz decided that he would only eat the fruits of *Eretz Yisrael*, which were blessed with a special sanctity.

But this was a year of drought in which no rain fell; the people of Tzefas found that they had to import flour for their daily bread. And still, R' Avraham Tzvi refused to bring anything that had not grown on holy soil to his mouth!

People were concerned for his health and begged him to make an exception, considering the difficult situation. But he was firm, explaining: "The Torah already foresaw the difficult times of the *shemitah* sabbatical year, when working the land was forbidden. 'What will we eat in the seventh year?' people would ask. Did the Torah offer the simple advice of importing food from abroad? Certainly not! Apparently then, that is not the answer!"

Better Late Than Early!

"וּזְרַעְתֶּם אֵת הַשָּׁנָה הַשְּׁמִינִת"

And you shall sow in the eighth year (25:22)

It was the year 5713 (1952), the year following *shemitah*. The settlers of Komemiyut had survived the past year on faith and miracles. But now that *shemitah* was over, they must resume farming and make up for lost time. In *Eretz Yisrael* it is important to get the plowing and sowing done before the winter rains begin falling, before the ground turns to mud. Once the seeds are safely in the ground and the rain falls, they can begin germinating to produce the year's crop.

The farmers of Komemiyut were very concerned this year that the rains would fall before they had a chance to plow and sow. The farms and kibbutzim all around had already done this before *Rosh Hashanah*, when it was still *shemitah*, not wanting to be caught by premature rains. But Komemiyut had waited. It was now *Succos*; there was a chill in the air. Rain might fall unexpectedly any day now.

The farmers came to the Chazon Ish just before *Succos* with a weighty question: might they be allowed to plow and sow on *chol hamoed*? If they sowed too late, they would forfeit that season's crop altogether.

The Chazon Ish was adamant and would not permit them to work on *chol hamoed*. He assured them that they would not sustain any damage by not plowing until after *Succos*.

"And who says that you will be too late? Perhaps, if you do plow on *Succos*, you will be premature and this will cause you real damage?"

The farmers listened to the Chazon Ish and, without a murmur of complaint, returned to their settlement. They did not plow on *chol hamoed*.

Succos passed. No rain. That year the rains did not begin falling until *Chanukah*. All the settlements which had planted early suffered huge losses. But the settlers of the religious settlement who had plowed and planted late, because they prized the holiness of *Succos*, were the only ones to reap a harvest that year!

Looking and Overlooking

"וּבָא גֹאֲלוֹ הַקָּרֹב אֵלָיו"

And his nearest relative shall come (25:25)

The Jews of Warsaw were very surprised when they found the great R' Akiva Eiger, who was visiting their city, wandering around the alleys and side streets one fine day, searching for a certain address.

"Who is the Rav looking for? Can we be of any help?" they asked.

R' Akiva shook his head. "No, thank you. I would like to make this visit myself. I have a relative living here in Warsaw whom I have not yet seen. I want to visit him."

When the townspeople inquired who this relative was, they were very surprised. R' Akiva was planning to visit a simple fellow, a laborer without even a smattering of Torah scholarship.

"But, Rabbi!" they said. "Is it not beneath your dignity to go to visit such a common fellow, even if he is your relative? Must a man of your stature and learning lower himself? The rabbis learn that there are certain times when a *talmid chacham* is exempt from fulfilling a *mitzvah*, if it is beneath his dignity, such as returning lost property. Rashi says that an old or a distinguished person must not drag along a lost sheep or goat to its owner since it is not befitting. The word used in the Torah is *'vehisalamta* — and you shall overlook'. (The simple way of understanding this verse is to treat it as a question: 'And shall you overlook such an opportunity to do a *mitzvah*?! Normally, one must never dream of overlooking it, but applied to a distinguished person the verse is taken as a command: 'And you *shall* overlook!')."The rabbis say that the Torah tells us that there are times when one may and should 'overlook' a *mitzvah*."

R' Akiva Eiger answered, "The word *lehisalem*, to overlook, appears in two places in Tanach: in the topic of lost articles, as you noted, and with regard to relatives — 'And you shall not overlook your own flesh.' An elderly person or a scholar need not return lost articles, but one should not overlook one's own flesh and blood, regardless of one's own dignity!"

Distant Relatives

"וּבָא גֹאֲלוֹ הַקָּרֹב אֵלָיו"
And his nearest relative shall come (25:25)

Reb Meir lived from hand to mouth. He never had enough to satisfy the hunger of his family and, surely, was not able to put anything away for a rainy day. Now that his daughter was of marriageable age, what was he to do? Where would he find the enormous sum to cover even a modest dowry and wedding expenses? He could not even begin to think of it. And so, his daughter sat at home, in her rags, getting older by the day.

But Reb Meir was fortunate on two accounts. He had a

rich relative and R' Yosef Zundel of Salant was his rabbi.

When he saw that Reb Meir was refusing all offers for his daughter's hand, R' Yosef Zundel went to R' Meir's rich relative and described the poor man's plight. "You must help Reb Meir out," he said. "As a relative, it is your duty."

The rich man, known to be tight with his money, shrugged his shoulders. "I am sorry, Rabbi, but I cannot give such a huge sum for a relative whom I hardly know. He is really a very distant relative."

R' Yosef Zundel changed the subject. "As a good Jew, I am sure that you pray three times a day. Tell me, how does the *shemoneh esrai* begin?"

"Are you making fun of me? I am not a child. I know how that prayer begins. *Baruch ata... elokei Avraham, elokei Yitzchak...*"

R' Yosef Zundel interrupted him, "Very good. Now tell me, when did these ancestors live?"

"Three thousand years ago. But what's the point?"

"Listen here. Your forefathers lived a few millennia ago and, yet, you mention them three times a day in your prayers. Why? Because you know, that in their great merit, you will also be blessed and protected. And, yet, when I ask you to help a poor relation marry off his daughter, a man who lives here and now — you claim that he is too distant!"

The rich man was struck speechless. Shortly afterwards he sent the money to cover all the necessary expenses.

The Chafetz Chaim Speaks

"וְכִי יָמוּךְ אָחִיךָ... וְהֶחֱזַקְתָּ בּוֹ... וָחַי עִמָּךְ"

*And if your brother shall become poor and his means fail... You
shall support him (25:35)*

"**R**abbenu! What are we to do? *Pesach* is just
around the corner. The city of Radin has many
poor people who will not be able to buy *matzos* and wine
without the community's help, but the community does
not have any funds. We have made a *ma'os chittin* appeal,
but the money trickling in does not even begin to cover
our needs. What should we do?"

The charity treasurers had come to the Chafetz Chaim,
by now an elderly man, begging for his assistance.

"Something must be done at once!" the Chafetz Chaim
agreed. "Call a public meeting in the central synagogue. I
want everyone to attend."

When the people of Radin heard that the Chafetz
Chaim had ordered the meeting, they all came to hear
him. "What did he wish to tell them?" they wondered.

The Chaftez Chaim walked slowly up to the platform
and looked around at the people of Radin with his kindly
but piercing eyes. Then he began, "My dear friends: As
you can see, I have been blessed with many years. I am
already old, not far from the World of Truth. What will
happen when I am summoned to the final judgment? I
will surely be asked about the people of my city. 'Do they
give charity?' the heavenly court will inquire. I truly don't
know what answer I will be able to give. If I say that the
people of Radin are charitable, I will be telling a lie. My

friends, I have never knowingly told a lie and I do not wish to begin doing so, especially in the World of Truth. And if I say that you — the sons of Avraham, Yitzchak and Yaakov — are stingy and do not give enough charity, this will be *lashon hara*, evil gossip, and I have always avoided that sin like fire.

"My dear friends: if you give generously to the community's *ma'os chittin* fund, so that the poor of our city can enjoy the festival properly, then, when the time comes, I will proudly be able to testify with a clear conscience that you are truly charitable."

The large hall was suddenly filled with a rustling as purses and pocketbooks were opened, bills were collected and checks were written.

The *gabbaim* of Radin's community chest later related that never did the people give so generously as they did then — neither before nor after!

"Small wonder," the townspeople would comment. "The Chafetz Chaim's moving words melted people's hearts and opened their purses."

A Valid Argument

"וְכִי יָמוּךְ אָחִיךָ... וְהֶחֱזַקְתָּ בּוֹ... וְחֵי אָחִיךָ עִמָּךְ"

And if your brother shall become poor... You shall support him... And your brother shall live in your midst (25:35)

The disciples of R' Yeshayele Mushkat of Prague had a question which disturbed them. They had learned that a person's life span is determined in heaven at his birth. And yet, they were taught by the wisest of all men, Shlomo Hamelech that 'charity saves from death'. How was this possible?

R' Yeshayele solved their problem. "When one gives more to the poor than he can afford, he can argue before *Hashem*, 'Just as I help the poor beyond what I can really spare from my own needs, so do I ask You, Who apportion life to all living creatures, to grant me more years than have been allotted to me.' "

Charity Adds Years of Life

"וְכִי יָמוּךְ אָחִיךָ... וְהֶחֱזַקְתָּ בּוֹ... וְחֵי אָחִיךָ עִמָּךְ"
*And if your brother shall become poor... You shall support
him... And your brother shall live in your midst (25:35)*

Everyone trusted Binyamin Hatzaddik. They saw how he distributed charity right and left to all the needy people in his city. Before long, people were giving him their *tzedakah* money, so that he could give it to the people who needed it most. Thus Binyamin Hatzaddik became the charity treasurer of his city. Huge sums passed through his hands; he collected from the rich and gave to the poor.

One year there was a famine. People who ordinarily did not need charity now came to R' Binyamin begging for money to buy food. As long as money remained in the charity fund, R' Binyamin gave.

However, after the last coin had been carefully distributed, a poor widow came crying to Binyamin. "I have seven orphans to support," she said. "If you do not help us, we will starve to death."

Surely, he could not turn her away! R' Binyamin took money from his own purse and gave to the widow. And, from then on, he continued supporting her out of his own pocket. Week after week, he would give her enough money to keep her family from starving.

Time passed. Binyamin Hatzaddik suddenly became ill. At first the doctors had hope, because he was still a young man. But he grew weaker and weaker and did not respond to any treatment.

Binyamin was on his deathbed; his hours were numbered. The angels were in an uproar. How could this precious soul be allowed to leave the earth when it had accomplished so much? They thronged before the heavenly throne to plead for him.

"Master of the World! This man has been supporting eight souls — a widow and her seven orphans — out of his own funds. We have been taught that You created Adam, the first man who populated the entire world, as a single man to show that whoever saves even one person saves an entire world! What about Binyamin, who saved eight worlds and now lies on his deathbed?"

Hashem accepted the argument and the plea. He rewarded Binyamin Hatzaddik with an additional twenty-two years of life, for the twenty-two letters of the *alef-beis* with which the Torah is written.

(According to Bava Basra 11a)

The Rejected Gift

"אַל תִּקַּח מֵאִתּוֹ נֶשֶׁךְ וְתַרְבִּית"

You shall not take from him interest or usury (25:36)

In a town near Pressburg lived a man who was as stingy as he was rich. The people of his village had learned not to ask him for charity since squeezing a penny out of him, for even the most worthy cause, was like squeezing water out of a stone. The wheel of fortune turned, however, and he lost all of his money and fell heavily in debt. But his neighbors would not help him for they well remembered his stinginess.

When he saw that he would get no aid from his fellow townspeople, he decided to go to the Chasam Sofer who lived not far away, in Pressburg, and ask for help.

The Chasam Sofer listened to his story. He saw before him a troubled Jew, a once wealthy Jew who had fallen on difficult times. His heart opened up in pity, without a thought of his past stinginess.

"And so you need a loan?" he asked. "You want to buy merchandise at the Pressburg fair? Let me see."

He opened up his drawers, hoping to find some money, although he knew that he had distributed the last penny, just yesterday. But he felt that he must help him. He went over to the silver chest, took out several pieces and gently put them in front of the troubled man.

"Here, take these. Sell them and be sure that you get their full worth. They are pure silver. Take the money and buy some merchandise. With *Hashem's* help, you will succeed in paying off all your debts and regaining your former wealth."

With *Hashem*'s help and with the Chasam Sofer's blessing, the man did extremely well, far beyond his expectations. When he had sold all of his merchandise and paid back his debts, he returned to Pressburg, to the Chasam Sofer.

"How can I ever thank you, Rebbe!" he said. "You saved me! Thanks to your blessing, I have regained my wealth. I have come to return the money that I owe you."

He laid out the sum on the table. Then, he withdrew a small box from his waistcoat, unwrapped the tissue paper and pressed it into the Chasam Sofer's hand.

"Here, I have brought you a small gift in appreciation."

The Chasam Sofer opened the box and gasped, the 'small gift' was a beautiful, sparkling diamond. He took the diamond over to the window and turned it around and around so that it could catch the sunlight in all of its facets.

"Ahhh! What a magnificent gem! This must be worth a fortune! It is unbelievably beautiful!"

Several *talmidim* were in the room at the time. They could not contain their surprise — and horror. Never had they seen their master and teacher so enthusiastic over a material object. Was the Chasam Sofer really going to accept this gift? It was *ribis*, interest on a loan, a sin strongly prohibited by the Torah. Could the Rebbe be so carried away by the beauty of the diamond that he had forgotten? That was unbelievable. The students murmured among themselves, repeating the word *ribis* again and again.

The Chasam Sofer, finally, turned to the merchant and said, "It is a truly phenomenal gem. You must have forgotten, though, that accepting a gift for a loan is forbidden by the Torah. It is interest. It is kind of you to be so grateful, but you surely do not want me to commit a sin. Take your jewel and go home. May *Hashem* continue to bless you."

As soon as the merchant had left, the Chasam Sofer turned to his *talmidim* with a smile and said, "Tell me, how often would I have an opportunity to fulfill the *mitzvah* of not accepting *ribis*? *Hashem* presented me with this precious jewel, beautiful to look at, of priceless worth. I was able to perform the *mitzvah* and not accept *ribis*. What joy!"

The Candle That Gave No Light

אֶת שַׁבְּתֹתַי תִּשְׁמֹרוּ"
You shall keep My Shabbosos (26:2)

The saintly R' Nachum of Chernobyl did not sleep much on Friday nights. He remained awake until very late, studying Torah. In order to be able to do so, he would light a large, thick candle that would last through the night.

One Friday evening, when R' Nachum was out, a sudden wind blew out the candle. When the gentile servant noticed this, he quickly lit it again.

Some time later, R' Nachum entered the house. His family, already in bed, heard strange noises. The Rebbe seemed to be groping his way in the dark. There was a shuffling of feet, a bumping into furniture. They could even hear R' Nachum knock his head against a wall. "What was the matter?" everyone wondered. "Couldn't he see?"

His family came rushing out, not understanding why R' Nachum could not find his way. When he heard their footsteps, he asked, "Why is it so dark here? Who put out the candle?"

"But Father! The candle is burning as usual! Can't you see it?" they said.

"Well then," said R' Nachum. "something must have happened! The candle must have gone out and then been relit; the *Shabbos* was desecrated. That is why I cannot see its light."

The puzzle was finally solved when the gentile servant admitted to having relit the candle.

The Trick

"גְדֹל הָעֵצָה וְרַב הָעֲלִילִיָּה"
Great in council and mighty in work
(Haftorah Parashas Behar, Yirmiyahu 32:19)

The poor man who entered the study of the Saraf of Kotzk had an interesting story to tell.

"Rebbe," he began with a sigh, "I was not always as you see me now. I once owned a huge mansion of many

many rooms, each filled with a wealth of costly furnishings. Dozens of servants and maids were at my beck and call.

"For many years, I had a maid who served the family loyally, working industriously and saving every penny she earned. One day she came to me to ask a favor. There was a special lottery-insurance plan being offered then, whereby one invested a large sum which was guaranteed. In addition, the investor had a chance of winning a jackpot prize. My maid asked me to buy her such a lottery ticket, so that, in the event that she married, she would have a tidy nest egg. If she were lucky, she might even retire rich. After I had bought her the ticket, I wrote the number down, as she requested, and checked the posted lists, periodically, to see if her number had been drawn for a grand prize.

"Years passed and the maid was as yet unmarried. My wife died during that period and my fortune began dwindling away until I fell heavily in debt. Once, as I was passing the bank, I noticed the latest lists announcing the winners of the most recent drawing. I checked the numbers against the one I had written down and, to my great surprise, discovered that the maid had received the jackpot prize of one hundred thousand ruble! My mind began whirling. I would marry her; the money would be mine! I would not disclose the fact of her winning until some time after the wedding, so as not to appear like a money-grubber.

"I proposed marriage and she accepted. Several weeks after our marriage I came home one day with the good news. Her ticket had finally come up in the lottery. She had won the first prize. We were fabulously rich. To my surprise, however, she did not react with the joy I had expected. 'What is the matter?' I asked. 'Don't you want to be rich?'

"With a weak, faint voice, she explained, 'I gave the ticket to my father several years ago. He sold it and built himself a house with the money.'

"And now Rebbe," the man concluded in a bitter tone, "I want to give her a divorce. It was all a mistake. I freely admit that I married the maid because I thought she had money. But she is really far below my station; she is a maid while I... Well, in short, I don't want her. Can you give me a divorce on the grounds that I was deceived?"

The Kotzker Rebbe was amused, "Do you know, this woman was destined to be your wife. But *Hashem* had to resort to a trick to deceive you into marrying her. Do you think that you can outwit Him? No, my dear friend. In marrying her, you were carrying out the Divine purpose. You cannot get around that. You deceived, but were deceived in turn. Accept your fate gracefully and make peace with it."

פָּרָשַׁת בְּחֻקֹתַי

Parashas Bechukosay

Only Torah!

"אִם בְּחֻקֹּתַי תֵּלֵכוּ"

If you shall walk in My statutes (26:3)

You should labor at studying Torah

(Rashi)

He was more than a lad but not yet a man. Still, Eliezer could not even read! His father, Hyrkinos, had worked hard all his life to acquire wealth and position. He had had no time for study. His sons too, worked industriously, tilling their father's land. Hyrkinos had not seen the need to teach them anything. They would not become scholars, but would remain on the farm.

He once discovered his young son, Eliezer, sitting on a rock, weeping.

"Why do you weep?" he asked. "Is it perhaps because I assigned you such difficult terrain to plow? Your brothers are plowing the plain while you must plow the stony hillside. Perhaps, I have not been fair. Tomorrow you will plow the plain and they will work the hillside."

The next day Eliezer worked behind the plow on the plain. But here, too, his father found him weeping. "What nonsense is this?" he asked. "I gave you the easiest land to plow and you still complain! What do you want?"

"I want to study Torah!" the youth sobbed. His father laughed. "Now! At your age? Are you a fool? If I had wanted to make a scholar out of you, I would have sent you to school when you were young. It is much too late. If you have such respect for learning, wait until you marry. Then you can send your own sons to school."

Eliezer would not give up. "I want to go to Jerusalem and study under the great rabbis!" he insisted. "I want to study under R' Yochanan ben Zakkai. If I am able to plow a stony mountainside full of boulders, I will surely be able to use my strength and determination to study Torah!"

"Don't be a fool! Now go back and plow your field. You will not get anything to eat until the work is finished. I will teach you to daydream!" Hyrkinos thought that, if he put his son to work, Eliezer would forget all of his ridiculous notions.

Eliezer awoke early the next morning and went to plow the field. He must first obey his father. That afternoon, when the field was all plowed, he left. But he did not go home. Instead he took the road to Jerusalem.

It was a long way and he went every step of it by foot. When hunger assailed him, he stuffed clods of earth into his mouth and chewed them to get the illusion that he was eating.

When he finally arrived, he went directly to the *beis midrash* of R' Yochanan and sat down on a bench. The great rabbi was expounding Torah before many students. But, Eliezer did not understand a word. He was terribly discouraged. Would he ever acquire any knowledge? Deeply frustrated, he began weeping silently.

R' Yochanan noticed the weeping youth. "Why are you crying?" he asked kindly.

"I want so much to study Torah, but I do not understand a word that you said, Rebbe!"

R' Yochanan asked, "What do you know? Have you ever learned anything?" Eliezer replied, "Nothing!"

"Well then, it is not too late now! I will teach you the *shema, shemoneh esreh* and *bircas hamazon*. Review them over and over, then we will proceed to other things."

R' Yochanan began teaching Eliezer, who proved to be an earnest, diligent and apt student. Day and night, he would review what he had learned and each morning he would be ready for the next lesson. Several days had passed when R' Yochanan noticed a terrible smell coming from Eliezer's mouth. He immediately guessed that the youth had not eaten for a long time. R' Yochanan questioned him directly, but Eliezer was too embarrassed to answer and just shrugged his shoulders. R' Yochanan then sent some of his students to Eliezer's lodgings to find out if he had dined there. When he discovered that Eliezer had not eaten for eight days, R' Yochanan immediately summoned the new student to him and said,

"Eliezer, my son! Just as a foul smell issued from your mouth now, so will your good name be on the mouths of all of Jewry in praise. You will yet become a famous Torah scholar and pearls of wisdom will drop from your lips! And from now on you will dine at my table!"

R' Eliezer remained in R' Yochanan's *beis midrash* for many years, learning day and night, until he became a great and famous scholar.

Once, R' Yochanan celebrated a festive occasion. All of the prominent men of Jerusalem were invited to partake in the feast. In the midst of the celebration, when everyone was seated and R' Yochanan was expounding, a visitor entered. R' Yochanan recognized him to be

Hyrkinos, R' Eliezer's father.

"Make way at the head table for Hyrkinos," he said. Hyrkinos took a seat among the other distinguished people. He was, after all, a wealthy man. He did not realize, though, that he was being honored because of his son.

R' Yochanan now indicated to one of his students to rise and speak. It was R' Eliezer! At first his father did not recognize him, never having expected to find him here! In fact, he had come to Jerusalem to bar Eliezer from inheriting any portion of his wealth. But there was Eliezer standing in front of this distinguished audience, spouting pearls of wisdom which no mortal ear had heard since the giving of the Torah at Sinai! Hyrkinus was stunned! And when his son had finished, R' Yochanan himself rose and planted a kiss upon his forehead!

Hyrkinos was deeply moved. He now arose and addressed the assembly, explaining the purpose of his visit. "I had intended to cut off my son from all my wealth, since he ran away from home and cut off contact, all these years. But, now, that I see that he has become an eloquent scholar, I bequeath all of my possessions exclusively to him!"

R' Eliezer put out a hand, as if to resist his father's impulsive gesture. "Father," he said, "had I wanted gold and silver, I could have prayed for them from *Hashem*. But I shun riches and have no use for them. All I desire in this world is to devote myself to the Torah. Leave your wealth for my brothers who will appreciate it. I have what I most desire — Torah!"

R' Eliezer remained in Jerusalem and continued learning until he became a teacher for all of Israel.

(Adapted from Pirkei d'R' Eliezer, Chapter 1-2)

The Unnecessary Servant

"אִם בְּחֻקֹּתַי תֵּלֵכוּ"

If you shall walk in My statutes (26:3)

You should labor at studying Torah

(Rashi)

The outstanding diligence and dedication to study of R' Avraham Shmuel Binyamin Sofer, better known as the Ksav Sofer, were exceptional, even while he was still a young child. The more he gained in knowledge, the stronger became his devotion to every precious moment of study. He was a living fulfillment of our Sages' directive to 'labor in Torah'.

As rabbi of Pressburg and head of its *yeshivah* he was busily involved in communal affairs. Nevertheless, each night, he would awake at two o'clock and study until time for *shacharis*.

Afraid that he might oversleep, the Ksav Sofer asked a gentile servant to peek into his window each morning at 2 a.m. If he did not see the candle burning, he was to enter and wake him.

After the Ksav Sofer passed away, the gentile servant related that in all the many years of his service to the 'Rabinner' he never once had to wake him up at night!

Two For Charity

"אִם בְּחֻקֹּתַי תֵּלֵכוּ וְאֶת מִצְוֹתַי תִּשְׁמֹרוּ"

If you walk in My statutes and observe My mitzvos (26:3)
"If you walk in My statutes" — you are guaranteed to
continue to do so. "...and keep My commandments..." —
for one mitzvah draws another in its wake.

(Commentaries)

"**L**et no one say that I do not give charity," said
Reb Berel.

He was a notoriously stingy person, who had come by
his riches by carefully saving each penny; he hoarded his
wealth and would not part with it. And yet, he did not
want the reputation of not giving. Many years before he
had set aside one penny for charity. Whoever came to his
door in those days was offered that one penny. No one
accepted such a paltry sum. It was beneath even the
poorest beggar's dignity to accept a lone penny from such
a wealthy person. And so, each time, the penny was
returned to its iron strongbox to await the next pauper.
Over the years this copper coin had turned green with
tarnish and was hardly recognizable. But when those who
did not know better came asking for charity, Reb Berel
would let them know that they "could take this penny or
leave it."

One day Berel's little Russian village was filled with
excitement. That evening a wedding was to take place, a
special wedding of two orphans who had lived in the
village all their lives. Everyone was involved in some way
or another in establishing a home for the young couple
who had no family to help them out. One had donated a

table, another chairs, a third had given them a pair of goosefeather quilts and pillows. It was a communal project. As for the wedding feast itself, this one baked; the other cooked. There was not a single resident, rich or poor, who did not have a part in the coming festivity. No one, except, of course, Berel.

Perhaps, if someone had approached him, he would have offered his green penny again. But who would even dream of making that ridiculous gesture?

In those times, each village had to produce its quota of soldiers for the Czar's army or pay five thousand rubles per head to free each man drafted. But no one dreamed that the ax would fall on this day!

That afternoon the chief of police came to the *chasan*'s house to take him away. A rabid anti-Semite, he gleefully picked this time to pluck the unwitting young Jew from his village and thus cause the most damage and heartache possible. The victim was given some time to pack his things.

The frightful news spread quickly throughout the village. People gathered here and there in groups, helplessly trying to find a way out of the dilemma. They drew near the house from which in a few hours they were to have taken the *chasan*, amid song and dance, and from which he now would be taken to the army.

This mix of sorrow, worry and pain met the visitor who came to town that afternoon. R' Shneur Zalman of Liady, the Baal HaTanya had come to gladden the hearts of the orphans on the day of their wedding. But instead of gaiety, he found gloom and despair, sighs and tears.

"Don't worry," the Rebbe reassured the townspeople, "*Hashem* will help, but we must get busy and do something too!" He went to the house of the rabbi to consult with him. The first step, they decided, was to go to the chief of police. Perhaps, he would agree to a lesser sum. Perhaps, he would allow the draft to be deferred to a later date. Perhaps, if they described the matter...

But no! This was his moment of glory. The police chief gloated in refusing all of their requests. "The young man will remain in our custody until the entire sum is produced; all five thousand rubles!"

"We should be thankful that he agreed to accept money," the village rabbi said to the Baal HaTanya as they left the police station. "But, where are we to get such an enormous sum?"

R' Shneur Zalman comforted him, "Leave it up to the Father of all orphans. *Hashem* will not abandon the *chasan* in his time of need."

At the rabbi's house they quickly drew up a list of all the rich men in the village. Next to each name they wrote the sum which he might be expected to give. When they finished, they added up the sums. The total did not even reach one thousand rubles!

R' Shneur Zalman skimmed through the list, then noted, "You forgot all about Berel! He surely is very wealthy. He must be made to contribute his part too!"

The rabbi laughed bitterly, "Ha! Berel? You mean Berel the miser? All he ever offers is his one penny, green with age, which is always refused. Of what good will that be? It's a pity to even waste your breath on him!"

"Nevertheless, I insist that he be put on the list. He is a Jew like the rest of us!"

"Very well," the rabbi sighed, knowing that it was a futile gesture. "I will put him on the bottom of the list. We can visit him last."

"No! I insist that he be put on the very top of the list!"

the Baal HaTanya said emphatically. The rabbi put Berel on the top. Their preparations concluded, all that was left was for them to begin making the rounds and hope for the best.

Since Berel was on the top of the list, they visited him first. Berel saw them coming from afar. He answered their knock immediately and ushered them inside.

The two rabbis were heartened by his courteous welcome. They sat down and began describing the plight of the orphaned bridegroom who had been drafted into the Russian army on his very wedding day. The miser was not unmoved. When they had finished, he went over to the niche where he kept his iron strongbox. He opened it up and withdrew the one ancient penny. This he gave to the village rabbi.

"Thank you very much!" R' Shneur Zalman hastened to say, thanking him profusely. "Thank you! May you be privileged to do many other worthy deeds! One *mitzvah* tows another *mitzvah* in its wake!"

They rose and went to the door and were about to leave when, suddenly, Berel had a change of heart. "Wait a minute! Here, perhaps I did not give you enough, worthy rabbis!" He handed them a whole ruble.

R' Shneur Zalman took the coin and thanked him, "May your *mitzvah* draw many other such *mitzvos* along, for one *mitzvah* tows another *mitzvah* in its wake!"

They again turned to go. They had hardly reached the door, when the miser came running after them. "Wait, my worthy rabbis! Wait a minute!" He was waving a ten ruble note in the air to make sure that they did not rush away. He stretched his hand out. R' Shneur Zalman took the note, saying once again, "Thank you very much. May you be privileged to perform many such good deeds for one *mitzvah* tows another *mitzvah* in its wake!"

Once more, they started to leave when, suddenly, they were again stopped. Berel called out, "Here! Take this too! I don't think I gave you enough." He opened his heavy iron strongbox, withdrew one thousand rubles and, as he gave it to R' Shmeur Zalman, Berel burst into tears. The dam which Berel had built in his heart over the years broke.

"The first time that I offered the penny to someone," he said, "he threw it in my face. I swore then that this penny would be my donation to whomever came asking for charity. Over the years, I offered it countless times and it was rejected time and time again. No one wanted it. It has lain in my safe, becoming greener and greener. And I, meanwhile, acquired the reputation of a miser until people stopped coming altogether!

"You, worthy rabbi of Liady, are the very first person to accept my single penny and to thank me for it. I am grateful to you for having allowed me to share in this *mitzvah*. And, now, that I have begun, I want to see it entirely through to the end. Here — take the entire sum!" He counted out five thousand rubles and gave it to R' Shneur Zalman. "As for the sum that I have already given you, the one thousand and eleven ruble and one penny — let that be a gift to the young couple!"

Without delay, the two rabbis rushed to the police station. They paid the entire sum, the prisoner was released and the young *chasan* was led from the police station directly to the wedding canopy.

Who can describe the joy that the entire community felt at that memorable wedding? Everyone felt as if the young bridegroom was his closest relative. Everyone rejoiced in his good fortune. And just as the *simchah* was at its peak, who should burst in, but a breathless messenger with the news that the chief of police had just been thrown by his horse and killed instantly!

On the following day the young bridegroom happened to pass by the town bridge when a bulky object caught his eye. He bent down and saw that it was a leather pouch. It had belonged to the late chief. He opened it up; there was a bundle of notes, the five thousand rubles which had been paid to ransom him, plus many other gold coins. He rushed to R' Shneur Zalman who was still in town to ask what he must do.

"The money is rightfully yours. Keep it and make the best use of it!" the rabbi ruled.

Many years passed. Once again, when R' Shneur Zalman was traveling through Russia to collect money for charitable causes, he happened to visit this small village. He went to the synagogue and asked for the names of people likely to help him in his worthy venture.

"There are two wealthy men in this village," he was told, "who will be glad to give to any worthy cause. One of them is Berel, who was once known as Berel the miser, but who is lavish when it comes to *tzedakah*. The other is a young man, an orphan, who came into a large sum of money on his wedding day and has grown wealthy. He, too, always gives generously. Be sure to visit them first."

R' Shneur Zalman smiled and nodded. And you can be sure that when he approached those two for donations he was not turned away emptyhanded!

Working for a Living?

"אִם בְּחֻקֹתַי תֵּלֵכוּ... וַאֲכַלְתֶּם לַחְמְכֶם לָשֹׂבַע"

If you walk in My statutes... You shall eat your bread to
satisfaction (26:3-5)

If you walk in My statutes — labor in Torah

(Rashi)

When Gavriel the innkeeper learned that the Chafetz Chaim was about to visit his town, he resolved to be the first one to offer him his hospitality. On the appointed day, he awoke early and went to the train station. To his good fortune, he was indeed the first to greet that great man and invite him to his inn.

As they were riding to the inn, the Chafetz Chaim turned to his host and asked, "How much time are you able to devote to study Torah each day?"

The man sighed and bowed his head shamefully, "Believe me, Rabbi, if only I had the time I would willingly study regularly. But as you must realize, earning one's living is very difficult these days. As our Sages said, the difficulty in earning one's bread can be compared to that of splitting the sea. I feel that in the flesh. I am up from early morning until late at night serving the guests at the inn. And, when I am finally ready to go to bed, I collapse, drained of all energy. I have no time or strength to learn, though I wish I did!

"This town is not far from Warsaw. Trains pass through here every hour. If I am not at the station to hustle up business, my competitor, the other innkeeper in town, will get all the customers. It is a hectic pace but that's life."

The Chafetz Chaim spoke sternly to him, "Pardon me, but you are like an ignorant peasant who has to go to the capital to arrange his affairs. The matter is very important and urgent to him. As he sits in the train, he becomes infuriated with its slow pace. He has no time to waste. Why doesn't the train travel faster?! Unable to bear it any longer, he rushes up from his seat and runs to the front of the train. He rolls up his sleeves, leans all of his weight on the front of the first coach and pushes with all his might. His face grows red, his breath labored, the sweat drips down his back.

"The other passengers watch him curiously and finally ask, 'What are you doing?' 'Well?' he replies, 'when my farm wagon is going up a hill and I want it to go faster, I push it from behind. Now, too, I am in a great hurry and want the train to travel faster. That's why I'm pushing!'

"The passengers smile at his naivete. 'Simpleton of a peasant,' they murmur. 'Do you really think that your meager strength means anything to the mighty engine running this train, that it makes a difference?'"

The Chafetz Chaim turned to his host and said, "Stop and think for a moment. Do you not realize that *Hashem* is running this world? *Hashem* operates this huge world with a power that is beyond human conception. He sustains every living thing from the greatest animals to the tiniest insects. And you, insignificant creature, have the presumption to think that with your puny efforts you can assist Him in sustaining you and your family?! You are but an infinitesimal cog in the great machine. Your most energetic efforts are not more than the exertions of the naive peasant pushing the train that is run by a massive engine! Instead of exerting yourself for your livelihood, you should rather devote your strength to the study of Torah which *Hashem* will not do for you. As for laboring to sustain yourself, leave that up to Him!"

The Chafetz Chaim's apt parable had the desired effect and, from then on, the innkeeper set aside fixed times for Torah study. Nor did his *parnassah* suffer in the least!

Blessed Rains

"וְנָתַתִּי גִשְׁמֵיכֶם בְּעִתָּם"

And I shall give you your rains in season (26:4)

Once, during the time of the *Beis Hamikdash*, there was a famine. The winter rains had not fallen. *Cheshvan*, *Kislev*, *Teves* and *Shevat* had come and gone, but still not a drop of rain. The grasses and shrubs had long since shriveled up and turned brown. Even the trees were dying. If the situation continued, people would die from lack of food and water.

The Jewish Sages proclaimed public prayer and fast days, hoping to arouse *Hashem*'s mercy, but still there was no sign of a cloud in the sky. Finally, they sent a delegation to Choni, a holy man, and begged him to pray for rain.

Choni received the delegation and promised to do what he could. After they had gone, he stood up and prayed. Nothing happened.

Choni picked up a twig and drew a circle. Then, he stepped inside it.

"Master of the world!" he said. "Your children depend on You! They have come to me, begging that I intercede

for them and pray for rain. They know that when I pray it is as a son beseeching his father. Surely You will not reject my prayer; Master of the world, I swear that I will not leave this circle until You have mercy upon Your children and send rain!"

Tiny droplets of rain began falling at once. A mere drizzle.

Choni's disciples came rushing to him. They were not at all pleased. "Rebbe, these drops are falling only in order to release you from your vow and enable you to leave your circle. But we need rain that will quench the thirst of all living creatures, rain that will soak the ground, fill up our empty cisterns, bring new life to all growing things. Pray for such rain!"

Choni turned his face heavenward and prayed, "Heavenly Father! This is not the rain I asked for. I want rain that will fill up all the cisterns, the wells and the rivers!"

Immediately, heavy black clouds released a torrent of rain. It poured down onto the earth, snapping dry branches, bending trees to the breaking point. Winds howled, lightning flashed and crashed and the pelting rain threatened to demolish houses. Water flooded the streets, sweeping everything which was not fastened down in its tide.

The *talmidim* turned to their Rebbe saying, "This is not the kind of rain we wanted either. Such a storm will wreck our houses and fields and bring destruction upon the world!"

Choni turned his heart to heaven once more and, like a son beseeching his father, prayed, "This is not what I asked for either! I want You to send rains of blessings, gentle rains, welcome rains, not harsh, hateful storms.

Rains to make the people rejoice!"

The storm subsided. The black clouds turned to grey and a gentle but steady rain began falling. It filled up the dry cisterns, the wells, the thirsty earth, the streams and rivers.

It rained and rained. Soon the water was overflowing. People living in the lower sections of Jerusalem were afraid that their homes would be flooded and fled to *Har Habayis,* the Temple Mount, for safety.

The *talmidim* came to Choni, once again. "Enough, Rebbe!" they begged. "If this continues, we will be flooded out of house and home. Before, you prayed for rain and were answered. Pray again. Pray that the rain stops, before it does any damage."

Choni shook his head. "My teachers taught me that one must not pray for a good thing to stop. These were blessed rains. They did you much good. But if you cannot bear it any more, I advise you to bring a thanks offering to the *Beis Hamikdash.* I will pray for you, too."

After the Jews had brought a sacrifice to the *Beis Hamikdash,* Choni began praying, "Master of the world! Your children are unable to bear too much good or too much bad, too much suffering or too much blessing. When You showed Your wrath by not sending any rain, they suffered greatly. And now, that You have sent bountiful rain, they cannot bear this either. May it be Your Divine will that this rain cease. It is enough."

No sooner had he finished praying than a brisk breeze began blowing, breaking up the clouds and sending them scampering. The sun shone upon a wet, glistening world, its thirst quenched. And once again the people were able to rejoice.

(According to Tractate Taanis 23a)

Aba Chilkiyah's Prayer

"וְנָתַתִּי גִשְׁמֵיכֶם בְּעִתָּם"

And I shall give you your rains in season (26:4)

L ike father, like son. Just as Choni was a holy man who had the power of bringing down rain, so did Aba Chilkiyah, his son, have that power, thanks to his righteousness.

In his time there once was a terrible drought. For almost a year no rain had fallen; the situation was desperate. And so, the Sages turned to Aba Chilkiyah, who, they knew, had special favor in heaven.

Two eminent scholars were chosen to ask him to pray for the Jewish people. When they arrived, he was not home. They went to the field and found him busily hoeing the ground.

"Shalom aleichem Aba Chilkiyah," they said. He did not reply, did not even look up at them. Surely he had heard!

The two scholars waited until he finished his work and followed him home. As they walked behind Aba Chilkiyah they noticed many strange things.

On one shoulder he carried a bundle of firewood. Across his other shoulder he carelessly threw a robe with which he might easily have cushioned his load. When he arrived home, he did not usher his guests in first, as courtesy required, but let them in after him. Aba Chilkiyah then sat down at the table with his wife, without inviting them to join him. And yet they were guests, who had come from afar.

When Aba Chilkiyah finished his meal, he turned to his

wife and said, "These *talmidei chachamim* have come to ask us to pray for rain. Let us go up to the roof and pray."

They both climbed up to the flat roof of their humble cottage. Aba Chilkiyah stood in one corner, his wife in another. Both began praying.

And behold! There was a cloud above the corner where Aba's wife stood. A brief moment later, and a cloud formed above the corner where Aba Chilkiyah stood, too, followed by rain.

Aba Chilkiyah went down to his two guests and said, "Thank G-d it is raining! Thank G-d, the rains came naturally and you did not need me to pray for you."

The two Sages smiled, "You need not deny your part. We know very well that the rains came because of your merit and your prayers! You caused *Hashem* to open up the treasurehouse of rain!

"And now, would you explain several unusual things which we saw today? Why didn't you reply to our greeting when we came this morning?"

"I am a day laborer," replied Aba Chilkiyah, and I am obliged to give my employer a full day's work. I must not waste any time."

The Sages continued to ask, "Why did you place the bundle of firewood on one shoulder and the robe on the other? Why didn't you cushion the unwieldy load with the robe?"

"It was a borrowed robe, lent to me for the wearing only, not for other purposes."

"Why did you have us enter your home after you?" they continued.

"Because I did not know you," he answered.

"And why did you not ask us to dine with you?"

"I had a good reason, you may be sure. There was not

enough food for all of us. I had not expected you. Had I invited you, you would have thought that I did so wholeheartedly. Since this would not have been true, I thought it better not to invite you altogether."

"And why did the clouds form above your wife's head first and not over yours?"

"That is because my wife is always at home when a poor man comes. She can give him food, which he can enjoy immediately and sate his hunger. I, who merely give money to the poor, cannot satisfy their hunger at once. The poor man must first buy food; he does not have immediate satisfaction. Thus, my wife's merit is greater. Her form of charity is more direct; it is instant."

The Sages left, thankful for the rain, and much, much wiser.

(According to Tractate Taanis 23)

In Whose Merit?

"וְנָתַתִּי גִשְׁמֵיכֶם בְּעִתָּם"
And I shall give you your rain in season (26:4)

It was a year of drought in the time of R' Yona, an *amora* who lived in *Eretz Yisrael.*

He saw how much his people suffered and his heart went out to them. Being a holy man, he knew that, if he would pray, *Hashem* would answer his prayers. But, being also a very humble person, he did not want anyone to know this.

Taking a shopping basket in hand with a sack in it, he told his wife that he was going out to buy some wheat.

He walked casually along until he came to the outskirts of the city. He continued on until he reached a desolate spot in the hills. Here, he put down his basket and took out the sack. He wrapped it around his body, then went behind some boulders to a hidden cave.

There, in secret, R' Yona prayed fervently.

While he was as yet in the midst of his supplications, the bright blue summer sky turned gray, then almost black; rain-soaked clouds gathered, filling the entire sky. It began raining, gently at first, then in earnest. The steady downpour became a torrent.

R' Yona finished praying, emerged from the cave and doffed the sack. Basket in hand, he rushed home, getting drenched, but loving it. When his wife heard him coming up the walk, she rushed to open the door. "Whew! What a flood!" she exclaimed. "Well, did you find any wheat?"

"No," he smiled. "We can afford to wait. I assumed that after such a rain, it won't be long before the new wheat grows. When the grain merchants realize this, they will stop hoarding their supplies and the price will drop. We have enough to last us until then."

And R' Yona did not tell a soul, not even his wife, that the rain had fallen because of his prayers.

(According to Ta'anis 23b)

The Lesson of the Hair

"וַאֲכַלְתֶּם לַחְמְכֶם לָשֹׂבַע וִישַׁבְתֶּם לָבֶטַח בְּאַרְצְכֶם"

And you shall eat your bread to satisfaction and you shall live
securely in your land (26:5)

There was once a *kohen* who found himself unable to support his family. He put his hand to different business ventures, but everything failed. Finally, one day, he made a momentous decision; he would go abroad. There was so much more opportunity there. People lived well abroad, it was known. He would try his luck in a new place.

He called his wife and announced his decision. "I know that it will be difficult for you. I may even be away for several years, before I can establish myself firmly enough to send you some money. You will have to raise the children by yourself during that time, but I know that you are a capable woman. There is, however, one thing in which I wish to instruct you; examining leprosy. You know that as a *kohen*, I am often consulted regarding skin disorders. Some sores are harmless and will pass by themselves. Others, however, where the skin and the flesh underneath have already died, are ruled leprous. You must refer such cases to another *kohen*, even though people will have to travel far to find one. Let me explain how you will know the difference, how you will be able to make the correct diagnosis:

You see, every single hair is nourished by its own separate source, its wellspring, so to speak, which is embedded deep in the skin. No two hairs share one source. If you see that any hair has dried up, lost its pigment, know that this means that the skin underneath is dead. This person must seek the expert guidance of a *kohen.*"

The woman heard this and said, "Do you hear what you are saying?! You just said that every hair has its own source of life and sustenance, independent of all others. You, who are the most complex creation on earth — man — do you think that *Hashem* did not create a wellspring for your needs?! Why must you go abroad when, surely, you can find *parnasah* here, in *Eretz Yisrael*? Put your trust in *Hashem*; He will sustain you, just as He separately sustains every single hair on a person's body! Stay here..."

The *kohen* agreed, "You are so right!" he said. "I will listen to you and remain. If I trust wholeheartedly in *Hashem*, He will reveal where my source of livelihood lies."

And indeed, the couple did prosper. The *kohen* tried his hand at something else and was successful.

(According to *Tanchuma, Parashas Tazriya; Vayikra Rabbah, Parashah 15*)

Why the Prince Cried

"וְאַף גַּם־זֹאת בִּהְיוֹתָם בְּאֶרֶץ אֹיְבֵיהֶם לֹא מְאַסְתִּים"
And yet for all that, when they are in the land of their enemies, I will not reject them, nor will I abhor them to destroy them (26:44)

New winds were blowing across Europe, winds of freedom and equality for all mankind. Governments of nations east and west were caught up in the new spirit of emancipation. Jews, who had been the most downtrodden of all peoples, welcomed the new equality for mankind. Finally, at last, they would enjoy the rights that all citizens had possessed all these years.

When the Chasam Sofer heard how people felt, he wished to set them straight. He clarified the matter by an apt parable:

A king once had an only son whom he spoiled and pampered. He gave in to the crown prince's every whim and when the tutors wished to punish him, the king would intervene. In time the prince grew up to be an impossible person and sought the company of evil companions. His father scolded him but it was already too late.

"I will send him away to a distant village to live with a common peasant," said the king. "There he will not be pampered. He will come to his senses and become mature. Then, when he is cured of his evil traits, he can return to the palace and to his honored place as crown prince."

The young prince was sent far, far away. He lived with a poor peasant, slept on a straw mattress, ate no more than coarse bread and worked hard for his keep. At first he found it unbearable. Each day was a fresh torture. But then, he began looking forward to the day when he would return home. His father did not despise him, after all, but only wanted to teach him a lesson. Some day, he would be returning to his father's palace!

Time did not pass quickly. Still, the prince always nursed that hope of returning home. How great was his shock when, one day, laborers from the capital arrived with building materials. First they marked off a large area. Then they dug foundations, poured cement and began construction. The prince went over to them and asked what they were building. "A palace," they replied. "For you, Your Highness." They thought that he would be overjoyed. The king no longer wanted him to live in a hut, sleep on a straw mattress, eat coarse food off coarse wooden plates. But instead of rejoicing, the crown prince wept.

"What is the matter? Are the plans not to your liking?" they asked the prince.

"Oh, it is very beautiful indeed! That is the problem! That is why I am crying!"

The workmen could not understand. The crown prince explained: "As long as I still lived in the peasant's cottage, working from early morning till late at night, I had hopes that my father would soon send to fetch me home. But, now, that I see him sending workmen to build me a permanent dwelling, I am truly distressed and discouraged! Who knows how long I will have to remain here now!"

The Chasam Sofer explained his parable. All of these privileges mean that our Heavenly Father is making it easier for us to remain in Exile. He does not want us back home yet! Equal rights will only sweeten the bitter pill of Exile. They will certainly not hasten the redemption.

He Neither Sleeps Nor Slumbers

"וְאַף גַּם־זֹאת בִּהְיוֹתָם בְּאֶרֶץ אֹיְבֵיהֶם לֹא מְאַסְתִּים"

*And yet for all that, when they are in the land of their enemies, I
will not reject them nor will I abhor them, to destroy them
utterly (26:44)*

Blood libel! The Jews of Spain were being accused of
having killed a gentile whose body had been found
in the courtyard of a Jew.

The body had been planted by a group of gentiles. The
guilty ones had then gone to the king, as a delegation
from the Christian community, demanding that he
prosecute the Jews.

They poured out their hatred against the Jews,
becoming so worked up that they said, "If the king does
not do anything at once, we will take the matter into our
hands! We will storm through the Jewish quarter,
massacring and plundering."

The king refused to swallow their poison and hatred.
He said, "I know that the Jews are innocent. You are
lying! Remain here and I will prove it! I will show you
that you yourselves have committed that terrible deed!"

The king then summoned the Jews in whose home the
body had been found and said, "Your King David said
that the Guardian of Israel neither sleeps nor slumbers. I
have asked experts in Hebrew what the difference is
between sleeping and slumbering. They say that the
terms are identical. If so, why does King David repeat

himself?"

The Jews were silent. They were confused. What did the king want?

"You have no answer," he said. "But I do! I know the explanation; I saw it with my very eyes just this past night.

"I was unable to sleep, try as I might. After fitful tossing and turning, I finally decided to go outside for a walk in my courtyard. As I strolled around, by the light of the full moon, I, suddenly, saw a group of men in a huddle beyond the hedge and looked out. One of them was carrying a corpse on his shoulder. I sent three of my servants to follow them without being detected.

"They did not disappoint me. They reported that the body had been deposited in the courtyard of these Jews who are now present. And do you know who carried the corpse and placed it there? These very men by whom you are accused!"

"And now," the king continued, "allow *me* to explain to you the difference between 'sleep' and 'slumber'. G-d, Who sits in heaven on high, never sleeps. But neither does He let others sleep if He needs them to protect His chosen people! Last night my own royal sleep was disturbed so that I might see what was happening with my own eyes. And now that I know the truth, they will suffer. Not the Jews!"

"With All Your Heart and Soul"

"אֲנִי ה' לֵב בֹּחֵן כְּלָיוֹת"

I am Hashem Who examines the heart and studies the kidneys
(Haftorah Parashas Bechukosay, Yirmiyah 17:10)

When the Baal Shem Tov once learned that there was a man who served *Hashem* even more perfectly than he, he longed to meet him and learn his ways. But heaven had not revealed to him who this person was, what he did, nor where he lived. As eagerly as the Baal Shem Tov wished to meet him, so did he know that there was a time for everything. One who pressured time was delayed by time. He must wait for the right moment.

The Baal Shem Tov did not forget. He waited patiently for a sign from heaven that the two great souls could finally meet.

Finally, that time arrived. The last *Shabbos* in *Elul* had drawn to a close. That night, at midnight, all of Jewry gathered in their synagogues to say *selichos*, to prepare themselves for the approaching Days of Awe — *Rosh Hashanah* and *Yom Kippur*. The Baal Shem Tov said *selichos* with great fervor. When he finished the prayers in the early hours after midnight, he ordered that the horses be harnessed and he set out on his way in company with his closest disciples. As soon as they left Mezibus behind them, his gentile driver dropped the reins, turned about on his seat to face the chasidim, allowing the horses to forge ahead on their own. The horses picked up speed and were soon skimming over the road, their hooves not even touching the ground. The chasidim felt as if they were flying through the air.

The morning star arose; the horses finally slowed down and came to a halt, as if they had been given a sign. The chasidim looked around, but did not know where they were. They seemed far away from civilization, in a field at the foot of a mountain. When dawn was turning into day, they got out, washed their hands in the dew drenched grass, and began the early morning prayers, inspired by the fresh morning air and the beautiful countryside.

Just as they had finished, they heard the sound of a *shofar* breaking the utter stillness. What a surprise! The chasidim looked all around and finally discovered a shepherd, enveloped in a fur cloak, standing on a rock some way up the mountainside, summoning his flock by that blast of the ram's horn. Slowly the woolly creatures were gathering around him, gazing lovingly up to their master. Flocks upon flocks came to wait patiently by a well, for the shepherd to give them water to drink. The shepherd looked at the large flock, at each and every sheep as if he remembered it personally. When he was satisfied that they were all present, that not one had strayed, he led them to the well. They waited patiently, while he filled the trough by the well. When it was about to overflow, he whistled, signalling them to begin drinking.

When the sheep had quenched their thirst, they scattered all over the field. The shepherd contemplated them with love and affection, seeing that they were all grazing peacefully. Then he lifted his eyes to heaven and said aloud, "A-mighty *Hashem*! You are the Creator of this beautiful world, of the heavens and the earth and of everything upon the earth. You are the Master and we are Your servants. To You must we give our thanks. To You must we offer our praises. I know, O *Hashem*, that You have one nation on earth. They are the sons of Avraham, Yitzchak and Yaakov, who pour out their hearts to You in prayer three times a day; morning, noon and evening.

"I, too, belong to this people and I, too, desire to serve You as they do. But I do not know how to pray. I became orphaned early in life and was brought up in a strange home, by the local landlord who owns the entire village. He did not bother to teach me to read or pray. As soon as I was old enough, he apprenticed me to the head shepherd where I was taught the only thing I know — to tend sheep. Beyond that, I know nothing!

"Still, I feel obligated to serve You. I will do so in the only way I know how. Here, I have this shepherd's horn. I will blow it with all my might, to show You how thankful I am to You."

The shepherd took a deep breath, then raised the *shofar* to his lips. He blew a mighty blast that echoed and reechoed all about. It was a steady long drawn-out sound that increased in volume, going on and on. All his heart went into the blast. Finally, the shepherd, all of his strength gone, collapsed to the ground. He lay there for several hours. When he came to himself, it was already noon. The sun was at its zenith. He stood up and climbed to the rock to gather his flocks together. It was time for them to drink again. He blew upon his horn and when they had all come, he went once more to the well to draw water and fill the trough.

When the sheep had been watered and had gone to their afternoon grazing, the shepherd again lifted his eyes to heaven and said, *"Ribono shel olam!* Merciful Father, Benevolent Master Who sustains all living creatures. I see how You provide for these sheep, for the people in the village where I live and for me. Thus do You sustain the entire world! How shall I thank You and praise You for everything? I know that You have a chosen people, descendants of Avraham, Yitzchak and Yaakov who worship You. I too, belong to that nation. But I do not know how to serve You, how to pray to You, as they do in their synagogues. How I wish I did! But there is something that I do know. I can sing shepherd's songs for I was taught this by the head shepherd. I will sing to You, O *Hashem* and hope that You accept this effort instead of prayer!"

He burst into song like a songbird, his clear voice imbued with a poignant longing and love which poured out from an overflowing heart. His sweet notes filled the clear air with an unearthly beauty.

The song touched even the grazing sheep. They lifted their heads, perked up their ears and listened in silence and wonder. The shepherd sang with all his might until he could no more. Then he sank to the ground, unable to move.

When he came to himself, it was already twilight. The sun had just set. The shepherd arose, climbed up the mountainside and summoned the sheep with a blast of his horn. He went to the well and again filled the drinking trough for his sheep.

They had finished drinking. It was dark. The entire world was reposing, at peace. The shepherd looked up and saw the stars twinkling. Unable to contain his

wonder, he burst out, "How great are Your works, *Hashem*! How magnificent! But I am such a small, insignificant creature in Your beautiful world. How I would love to praise You properly, to glorify You. But what am I, what can I do? I know how to blow my horn; I blew it for Your sake. I know how to sing and have sung for Your sake. But how puny are these efforts compared to Your greatness! I want to give You pleasure as You give me pleasure from Your great and beautiful world. How can I do this? How can I express the fullness of my heart when I am nothing more than a simple, unlearned shepherd?"

"What else can I do?" he mused thoughtfully. Suddenly, his eyes lit up. "I know! There is one thing that always amuses my master and everyone who sees it! I will do that trick for Your honor, *Hashem*! To please only You!"

The young shepherd then made a handstand and turned a somersault, then another and another, faster and faster. He resembled a turning wheel, a ball. One could not distinguish his head from his feet, so quickly did he turn. He whirled and twirled and, finally, falling to the ground, he lay there, motionless.

Some time later the shepherd revived. He stood up shakily on his feet, gazed heavenward, and said, "A-mighty *Hashem*! There is still one more thing which I wish to do for You. Yesterday my master, the landlord, invited all of his servants to a banquet. I was there, too. When it was over, he gave a gift to each employee — a coin. This coin is the only money I have ever possessed, the only thing that I can really call my own. I want to give You this coin as a gift, as an expression of my great love for You. Please, *Hashem*, accept my humble offering!"

The young shepherd took something out of his pocket

and threw it upwards with all of his might. And, suddenly, a fiery hand appeared in the dark sky, caught the coin and disappeared in a flash.

The shepherd was not finished yet. He gazed upward and spoke, once again, "I have heard, *Hashem*, that there is a reward waiting for all Jews who serve You, a portion in the World-to-Come. If such a reward awaits me, I wish to give it to You as a gift, to express my boundless love for You!"

The Baal Shem Tov and his *talmidim* had been standing nearby, watching this shepherd all day long, their amazement at his devotion growing from hour to hour. And now, the Baal Shem Tov, finally, turned to his companions and said, "Just look at this man's great love! Our Torah tells us to love *Hashem* with 'all our hearts, all our souls and with all our might.' See how this shepherd before us fulfills that commandment literally, perfectly. Would that we stood upon his exalted level! Would that we served our Creator with the same wholeheartedness as do all the humble people on earth who serve *Hashem*, but do not seek reward."

A Wise Man and a Fool

"עֹשֶׂה עֹשֶׁר וְלֹא בְמִשְׁפָּט בַּחֲצִי יָמָו יַעַזְבֶנּוּ"

He acquires riches but not justly, in the midst of his days he shall leave them
(Haftorah Parashas Bechukosay, Yirmiyah 17:11)

The Chafetz Chaim did not want to be supported by charity. His needs were very few, but he wished to earn his livelihood and so, decided to run a grocery store.

The weights and measures used were exactly accurate; he would only bring the freshest products into the store; he took only the barest minimum of profit. No wonder, then, that everyone in Radin flocked to his grocery store. Here a person could be sure of getting top quality merchandise at the most reasonable prices. And he surely need not question the storekeeper's honesty!

When the Chafetz Chaim saw that customers were coming to his store and abandoning their former grocers, he became upset. He certainly had not intended drawing them away from his competitors. He closed the shop for all, but a few hours each day.

But his customers complained. They came to him, saying, "Rebbe, we only wish to buy from you. Here we are certain that no one will cheat us. In all other grocery shops we are taken for fools. We are sold inferior products and we must be on guard all the time to get our money's worth. With you, Rebbe, it is different. We know that you are scrupulously honest, that your scales are exact and that we won't be fleeced."

The Chafetz Chaim refused to hear any more. "How can you speak against any other Jew? How can you accuse someone of trickery and dishonesty? Even if it once happened that a grocer made a mistake, and we are all human, you must not speak against him!"

The Chafetz Chaim was deeply disturbed by what the people had been telling him. He resolved to do something.

He called together a meeting of all the storekeepers in Radin and spoke to them, "You all probably think it very clever to dupe customers. You feel that you are the wise ones and they, the fools. In fact it is quite the opposite! By stealing a few pennies from a customer, a storekeeper actually causes himself great damage and loss, besides sinning against *Hashem* and against his fellow man!"

The storekeepers lowered their eyes. The Chafetz Chaim continued, "Let me tell you a parable: A Jewish merchant used to buy large quantities of flour from an illiterate gentile miller who did not know arithmetic. He became confused with larger amounts. In order to keep count of what he was selling the Jew, he made up a foolproof system. Each time he gave the Jew a sack, the latter would give him a small copper coin. After the Jew had set aside the amount he needed, the miller would count up the coins and receive a gold coin in exchange for each of the copper ones.

"This system worked well for a while. Whenever the Jew bought a large quantity, he laid out his copper coins and would then redeem each one by a gold one, the price of a sack of flour. Once the stupid miller decided to trick the Jew by slipping some of the copper coins into his own pocket. He thought that he was gaining these coins, but, in truth, he was really cheating himself, stealing from his own pocket! For when the reckoning was made, he was not paid with gold coins for the missing copper coins which found their way into his pocket.

"There are some storekeepers who think themselves clever, when they cheat and steal a few pennies here and there. Really, *they* are the fools for their loss far outweighs the gain of the few paltry coins. On the other hand, those who are scrupulously honest and who do not touch a penny that does not belong to them, they are the really clever men for they will benefit not only in this world, by gaining a good reputation, but also in the next world!"

The Doctor's Delay

"רְפָאֵנִי ה' וְאֵרָפֵא"

Heal me, Hashem, so that I will be healed
(Haftorah Parashas Bechukosay, Yirmiyah 17:14)

"**Y**ou must come at once, Herr Doktor! My father has had another attack!"

The young girl had rushed into the doctor's office without even knocking. Doctor Aharon Gardiya had saved her father's life several times before. If anyone could save the sick man, it was Dr. Gardiya, private physician to His Royal Majesty King Friedrich the Great of Prussia. Bursting in now, the girl fully expected him to follow her at once, without delay.

Why was he tarrying? The young girl stood nervously by while the doctor removed his white coat and took his jacket. He began brushing it leisurely, making sure that every speck of lint was gone. The girl urged him to hurry for her father had not long to live. But the doctor took his time. After he put on his jacket, he went to fetch his top hat. This he brushed carefully too, with gentle strokes so as not to ruin the fine nap. He turned it all around to inspect his work and when he was satisfied, put the hat back on the stand while he polished his shoes. He put on some work gloves and applied bootblack. Then he began brushing vigorously until they gleamed; he buffed them with a brush, then with a soft cloth until they looked like new.

The young girl could not stand this any longer. "My father is dying and you take your time with your hat and shoes! Oh, *Ribono shel olam*! If anyone can help him any more, it is only You, *Hashem*! Please, please let my father live!" Tears streamed down her cheeks.

This is apparently what the doctor had been waiting for. He put his shoes, hat and jacket aside and said,

"You can return home now. Your father has passed the crisis. He will live."

The girl rushed home and to her surprise, found that her father's condition had indeed improved. In the coming days he mended slowly, until he was completely recovered.

Later, when someone asked the doctor why he had refused to visit his dying patient, he said, "I knew the patient's condition well. His daughter's weeping state told me that medicine would not be able to help him; his life was in G-d's hands. I had to get her to pray. She did not need me any more; she needed the Divine Healer to help her father. And so I did my best to irk her by dallying with my clothing until her patience burst. That is when she turned to *Hashem* and began praying. And the heavenly Healer did not disappoint her..."

הַפְטָרוֹת מְיֻחָדוֹת

פָּרָשַׁת זָכוֹר
שַׁבָּת־הַגָּדוֹל
שַׁבָּת וְרֹאשׁ חֹדֶשׁ

Parashas Zachor
Shabbos Hagadol
Shabbos Rosh Chodesh

Fervent Prayer in a Compressed Atmosphere

"הַחֵפֶץ לַה׳ בְּעֹלוֹת וּזְבָחִים כִּשְׁמֹעַ בְּקוֹל ה׳"

*Does Hashem delight in burnt offerings and sacrifices as in
hearkening to the voice of Hashem?*
(Haftoras Parashas Zachor, Shmuel I 15:22)

It was *Rosh Hashanah*. The *beis knesses* was packed with
people and the air was stifling. R' Yisrael Salanter
looked all around the synagogue and noticed one young
man standing in the doorway at the other end of the *beis
knesses*. He waited until the young man finished his long
and fervent *musaf shemoneh esreh* prayer, went over, drew
him aside and said,

"I do not understand how you were able to stand in
the doorway and pray. See how full the synagogue is
today? Even old people who are ordinarily too weak to
come on *Shabbos* have come today. It is hot and stifling.
There is no air to breathe. Did you not realize that by
standing in the doorway you were stealing people's fresh
air? Imagine if someone had fainted for lack of air. You
would be to blame! You surely did not realize this, but
you should be sensitive to such things and not think only
of your own convenience."

A Mitzvah Without Self-Interest

"לִירְאֵי ה' וּלְחֹשְׁבֵי שְׁמוֹ"

For those who fear Hashem and thought upon His name

(Haftoras Shabbos Hagadol, Malachi 3:16)

If a man intends to perform a worthy deed but is prevented from doing so by outside circumstances, he is nevertheless credited with having actually done it!

(Tractate Berachos 6a)

A follower of R' Mordechai of Lechovitz once asked the Rebbe to be the *mohel* at his son's *bris*. The infant's grandfather, however — the chasid's father-in-law — was no admirer of the Rebbe and was strongly opposed to his being honored. In order to prevent this at all costs, he made a speedy *minyan* and performed the *bris* with a bare *minyan*.

When the child's father found out, he was furious, but there was nothing he could do about it. The *bris* had already been performed.

Later, at the *seudas mitzvah*, the young father and the other chasidim present could not help noticing how happy the Rebbe seemed. He was in elevated spirits, even more than at other circumcisions where he had actually been the *mohel*. They could not understand this, since he had been so insulted by the grandfather.

When R' Mordechai realized that people were looking at him in wonder, he offered an explanation for his unbounded joy, "As you must realize, the commandment of *milah* is a great one, but it is difficult to fulfill it purely for heaven's sake, without selfish motives. It is also known that if a person is prevented from fulfilling a good deed which he had intended to perform, he is still credited with having done it.

"Today I was supposed to have performed a *mitzvah* but was prevented from doing so. Still, the Torah guarantees that I will be rewarded as if I actually did it! In this case, I certainly had no ulterior motives so that my *mitzvah* is all the more acceptable and praiseworthy to *Hashem*. Should I not rejoice then, for having been credited with such a *mitzvah*?!"

The Second Half of the Garment

"גַּם־אֲנִי אֶבְחַר בְּתַעֲלוּלֵיהֶם"

Even so, I shall choose their mockings
(Haftoras Shabbos v'Rosh Chodesh, Yeshaya 66:4)

The following story appears in the book *"Niflaim Maaseicha'* by the Ben Ish Chai:

No one would have ever believed that the poor beggar who roamed the city streets was really the father of Zevulun, the successful businessman. Zevulun lived in a mansion, tended by dozens of servants. He ate the best cuts of meat, day in and day out.

And his father? He lived in a small shack, wore his old clothing and kept to his old friends. This hardly fitted in with Zevulun's standard of living. Zevulun was ashamed of the old man and one fine day, told him never to step into his home. Nor did he give him any money either. He let the old man live his own life. "I won't interfere with his life; he need not interfere with mine."

The old man grew feeble with age yet he had to beg for his daily bread. He grew shabbier, thinner until he was a mere shadow. And the worse his condition became, the less Zevulun wished to have to do with him.

One day, as he was sitting on a bench together with some fellow beggars, shivering in the winter wind, Zevulun's father spotted his grandson walking down the street. He beckoned to him and said, "Come here, my son. It's cold today, isn't it? I see that you have a warm coat against the cold weather. But all I have is this threadbare jacket. Please go home and ask your father to give me something warm to wear."

The little boy's heart went out to his grandfather. If only *he* could help him. But he knew how his father felt about the old man. The child went home with the message. At first Zevulun pretended not to have heard, but when the boy continued waiting, he finally said, "Go up to the attic. You will find a coat hanging on a nail. You can give that to your grandfather."

The little boy climbed up to the attic and looked around. He did not see any coat. All he could see was a motheaten rag hanging on the nail. But come to think of it, it must have been a coat once. Was *this* what his father had in mind for his grandfather?! The boy was appalled. He was too ashamed to bring this rag to his grandfather! His heart went out to his suffering grandfather. After a moment's thought, he came up with an idea. He took a pair of scissors and cut the coat into half.

Manwhile, his father was getting impatient. "What's keeping you?" he cried. "What are you doing up there?"

"Just one minute. I am almost ready," he called back.

Soon the boy descended from the attic with half a garment in his hand. "What is that?" Zevulun asked. "What have you done?"

"I cut the coat in half, Father," he said with pretended innocence. "I am saving half of it for you, for when you grow old. I will put you out of the house. You will roam the streets with the rest of the poor and when you ask me for something warm to wear in the winter, I will send the other half of this coat. Just as you behave to your father, that's how I will behave to you."

The father suddenly realized how disgracefully he had behaved. His own son had taught him a lesson. Ashamed of himself, Zevulun went out in person to find his father and bring him home. For good.

Whatever a Person Does, He Does For Himself

"גַּם אֲנִי אֶבְחַר בְּתַעֲלוּלֵיהֶם"

Even so, I will choose their mockings
(Haftoras Shabbos v'Rosh Chodesh, Yeshayah 66:4)

In the security of his palace, surrounded by ministers and advisors, how can a king know what is really going on in his kingdom, how people really feel towards him and his government policies? He knows only what he is told!

Therefore, a king who wished to know the true state of affairs would from time to time remove his royal cloak, doff his crown and don peasant garb. Dressed like a commoner, he could wander freely through the city and keep his eyes and ears open.

When the king passed through the marketplace in his disguise, he often went by a beggars' corner and like any other passerby, would throw a few coins into each metal cup. Each beggar would bless him for his kind heart — all except one strange man. Time after time, this beggar would say: "Everything that a person does, whether good or bad, is for himself." At first the king paid him no attention. But when he thought about it, that sentence irked him. Instead of blessing him like the others, this man was telling him that he was only being selfish — even when he gave charity. How could this be true? The man was an ingrate! The king would punish him.

The next time that the king put on his peasant disguise, he went directly to the marketplace and gave out his coins, as usual. The other beggars lavished praise on him. He went from one to the next, dropping a few clinking coins into their tin cups. Finally he came to the ungrateful beggar. Here he stopped, saying, "You, too, deserve some charity. I have a fine roast chicken for you. I am sure you will enjoy it!" Everyone looked at the browned, juicy crisp chicken and their mouths watered.

The beggar looked at the bird. He had never tasted roast chicken in his life! He considered himself fortunate, if he earned enough to buy some bread and a bit of oil to smear on it! At best, a piece of herring when he really did well. But chicken? Never! His eyes teared and his mouth watered at the sight of such a fine meal. How he longed to sink his teeth into this food of the rich, just once in his life! But this peasant must be making fun of him! Why would he want to give him a roast chicken?

"Here, take it! It's all for you. I really mean it! I want you to enjoy it!"

The beggar looked at it again, not daring to believe his

good fortune. Meanwhile all the other beggars swarmed around him jealously. The beggar stretched his hands out to take the gift, then said as usual, "Everything that a person does is for himself."

When the king heard this, he was enraged. There was no greater ingratitude that this! But he swallowed his anger with a pleasant smile and walked away.

The beggar was left holding the roast chicken. His nostrils quivered in eager anticipation. Roast chicken! A meal fit for a king! But he surely was not going to eat it right there in the middle of the marketplace, with everyone looking on hungrily, their eyes imploring him for a taste. No, such a fowl deserved a white tablecloth, some flowers in a vase and some vegetables to go along with it. He would take it home and eat it leisurely, in privacy.

Guarding the precious burden carefully, the beggar left his stand, the wafting aroma trailing behind him, reminding people that it was not a dream.

He stopped to buy a few vegetables and a small bunch of violets from an old woman selling flowers. He felt like a rich man today. What a feast he would have! Fit for a king!

He laid out a plain cloth, put the flowers in a glass of water and the chicken on a platter. He was, finally, about to sit down and take his first bite when, suddenly, he heard hoofbeats. "The king's hunters," he thought. They often came by this way since his cottage lay at the outskirts of the city, near a forest. He waited for the noise to die down so that he could eat in peace, but it didn't. He looked out of the window and saw that the hunting party was stopping at his house! At the head was the prince! He looked weary; he must have had a hard day at the hunt. But why was the retinue coming to his home? His heart skipped a beat in fear.

There was a loud pounding at the door. With quaking knees, he went to answer. The prince's aide stood there and said, "Let us in. The prince has had a sudden fit of weakness. He must eat something or he will faint."

What else was there for the poor beggar to do but give him the roast chicken! The prince, accustomed to such delicacies, fell upon it with gusto, not leaving even a bone to munch on. But as soon as he had finished, he gripped his stomach, gave a loud moan, and fell unconscious to the floor. The prince's servants tried to revive him, but it was too late. The prince was dead. He had been poisoned. They gazed at the beggar in horror. He had poisoned the young prince! He must be brought to justice!

They took the dead prince and the beggar back with them to the palace. The poor beggar was certain that he would be put to death. "Well, if he had eaten the chicken, he would have died anyway," he thought, "for it had been poisoned." He wondered why...

The beggar was brought before the king. Suddenly, the king realized that what this man had always said had now come true. He had intended to poison the beggar. And the evil he had planned had rebounded. His son was dead; in the end, it was the king who had suffered!

The king ordered the beggar released, turned to him and said, "Indeed, you were right — everything that a person does, whether good or bad, is for himself!"

Are We Really Waiting?

"שִׂישׂוּ אִתָּהּ מָשׂוֹשׂ כָּל הַמִּתְאַבְּלִים עָלֶיהָ"

Rejoice for joy with her, all you that mourn for her
(Haftoras Shabbos v'Rosh Chodesh, Yeshayah 66:10)

The people of Brisk had just sent a delegation with a *ksav rabbanus* begging R' Yosef Dov Ber Soloveitchik to become their rabbi.

But he was adamant. "I promised myself that after Slutzk, I would not take on another rabbinical position. That is final!"

The delegation was terribly disappointed. One of them could not control himself and burst out, "But Rebbe! Twenty-five thousand Jews are waiting for you; they are expecting you, relying on your coming! How can you disappoint twenty-five thousand Jews?!"

These fervent words spoken from the heart entered the heart. If that was the way it was... R' Yosef Dov went to the Rebbetzin and said, "Quick, fetch me my frock coat. I cannot refuse the delegation from Brisk. Twenty-five thousand Jews are waiting there for me to become their rabbi. I must not keep them waiting!"

The Chafetz Chaim, who happened to be there at the time, gave a deep sigh and said, "Just see how concerned R' Yosef Dov is not to keep twenty-five thousand Jews waiting! If only *Mashiach* knew that we, the entire Jewish people, were also eagerly waiting for him, would he not come running?! Surely he would not keep us waiting..."

R' Akiva's Consolation

"וּבִירוּשָׁלַם תְּנֻחָמוּ"

In Jerusalem will you be comforted
(Haftoras Shabbos v'Rosh Chodesh, Yeshayah 66:12))

Three Sages, Rabban Gamliel, R' Yehoshua and R'
Akiva, went up to Jerusalem. Even though the *Beis
Hamikdash* no longer stood, yet, the holiness of the city
drew them and they wished to pay their respects, at least
to its ruins, to share their feelings with the mourning
Zion.

When they finally approached the abandoned *Har
Habayis*, the Temple Mount, they saw stones strewn
about — and a fox slipping out from the ruins of the
Holy of Holies!

Rabban Gamliel and R' Yehoshua burst into tears. R'
Akiva laughed!

"Why are you laughing?" they asked in horror.

"And why are you crying?"

"Why are we crying?! Because the Torah said: 'The
stranger who approaches shall die.' Look! A fox runs
freely in and out of the holiest spot on earth! Shall we
not cry?!"

"And that is the very reason why I am laughing!" he
explained. "Just as the prophet's words about the *churban*
— Destruction — were fulfilled, that foxes would roam
through the *Beis Hamikdash*, so will their comforting
prophecies of Jerusalem's redemption and restoration also
be fulfilled!"

When they heard these words of consolation, Rabban

Gamliel and R' Yehoshua wiped away their tears and exclaimed, "Akiva! You have comforted us!"

(According to Tractate Makos 24b)